saw showcase

saw showcase

Science from the John Innes Centre and
the Institute of Food Research presented by children
from schools in and around Norfolk

Published by the SAW Trust
18 Lower Road
Rockland St Mary
Norwich
NR14 7HS
info@sawtrust.org

ISBN 978-0-9550180-2-2

Designed by Wiz Graphics
Edited by Jane Bulmer
Reprographics by Kevin Parker
Printed in Great Britain by Norwich Colour Print

Science, Art and Writing

a new way of looking at the world

Other SAW Trust publications:

see saw

An anthology of poetry and artwork around science

ISBN 0-9550180-0-5

Contents

Acknowledgements

SAW was initiated and developed by Anne Osbourn, founder of the SAW Trust (registered charity no.1113386). Anne Osbourn would like to thank everyone who took part in these projects, Helen Ghirardello (John Innes Centre) and the Communications Department (The Operations Centre) for their support, the Science Photo Library for supplying images, and Wiz Graphics for the design and assembly of this book. This set of SAW projects was funded by a grant from the Science and Society panel of the Biotechnology and Biological Sciences Research Council and by a Branco Weiss Fellowship award.

With thanks to the Teacher Scientist Network for support and provision of equipment for use in schools.

Introduction

Scientists are specialists. They have become hard-wired into jargon and use an exclusive vocabulary. To paraphrase Newton, they stand on the shoulders of giants, building on a mass of pre-ordained knowledge. They are intimately familiar with the most detailed of details in the area of research in which they work. Specialization is important. Specialized communities, be they of scientists, writers, artists, builders, electricians, plumbers, lawyers, doctors, teachers or others, provide a forum for efficient shorthand communication – an environment in which groups of specialists can function effectively. But if, during the process of specialization, we lose the ability to communicate with those outside our fields of expertise, then our value to society becomes compromised.

The path to specialization of knowledge starts early. By the time children leave primary school, they have already been taught to view science and the arts as separate disciplines, rather than as interlocking pieces that together lay the foundation for a deeper understanding of the world. These divisions are reinforced in high schools, where the constraints of the rigorously compartmentalized curriculum further isolate subjects, stifle inquisitiveness and quell creativity. And the question arises, how do we break down these barriers or prevent them from becoming established in the first place?

The Science, Art and Writing (SAW) initiative is an innovative science education programme that breaks down traditional barriers between science and the arts. SAW uses themes and images from science as a starting point for scientific experimentation, art and creative writing and, in doing so, stimulates creativity and scientific curiosity. Children realize that science and the arts are interconnected – and they discover new and exciting ways of looking at the world. In a recent BBSRC-funded set of SAW projects we took research science into schools, using SAW as a vehicle. Scientists from the John Innes Centre and the Institute of Food Research in Norwich worked with teachers, writers, artists (and, in one case, a musician) to run SAW projects based on their own research areas in schools in and around Norfolk. All 15 schools that took part in this programme of projects then came together to celebrate and share their experiences in an event held at the John Innes Centre in July 2008. This book provides a flavour of what happened.

Since the very first SAW project in 2005, SAW projects have been running in schools across Norfolk, elsewhere in the UK, in the US and in Italy. For more about SAW, please visit www.sawtrust.org

Anne Osbourn

GREAT

Nombres

sévère
bavard
bavarde
sympa

Streptomyces

Keith Chater
John Innes Centre

My whole working life has been spent studying bacteria of the genus *Streptomyces*. These bacteria are abundant in soil, where they play an important part in recycling the toughest parts of dead plants and fungi. They are generally particularly 'good' bacteria, both because of this ecological role and because they make many of the antibiotics that are used for the treatment of diseases. I am especially interested in understanding how they grow as branching filaments that eventually send reproductive branches up into the air, where they produce beautiful spiral chains of spores. Now that I have passed the age for retirement, I work part-time, mostly writing scientific papers and doing computer-assisted analysis of genome sequences.

streptomyces

Rockland St Mary Primary School

Teacher **Jess Hoare**
Age range of children **8-9**

Scientist **Keith Chater**
Artist **Tony Keeler**
Writer **Mike O'Driscoll**

The children loved the practical aspect of the science – microscopes, pH testing, smell tests. They also really enjoyed the writing and art.

Jess Hoare Teacher

There are about 1,0000000000 bacteria in a teaspoon of soil.

Kieran Crawford Age 8

Bacteria can be so colourful.

Oliver Wakefield Age 8

Amazingly, I observed something about how Streptomyces *colonies grow that had escaped my notice in the previous 39 years!*

Keith Chater Scientist

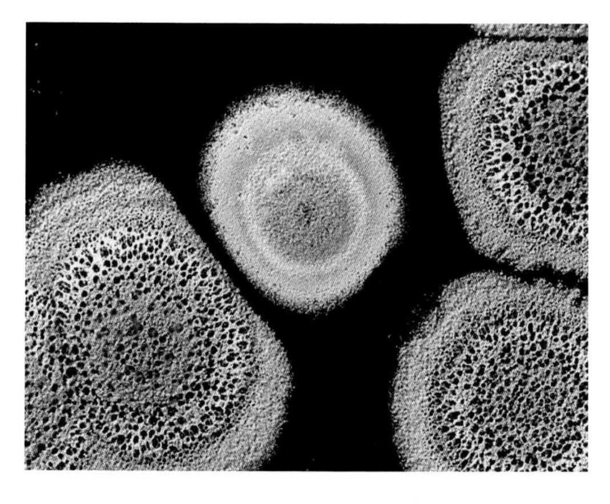

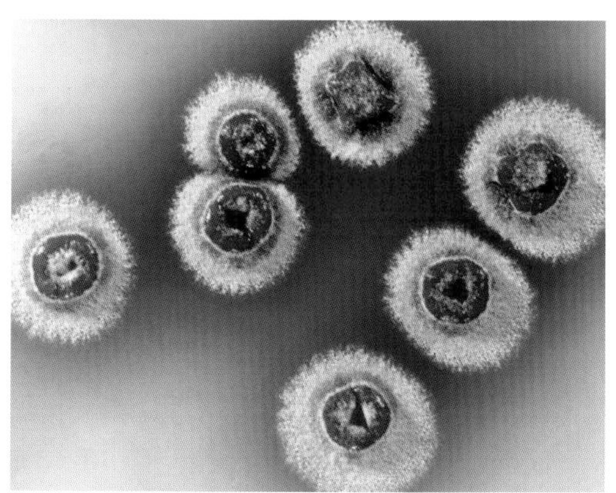

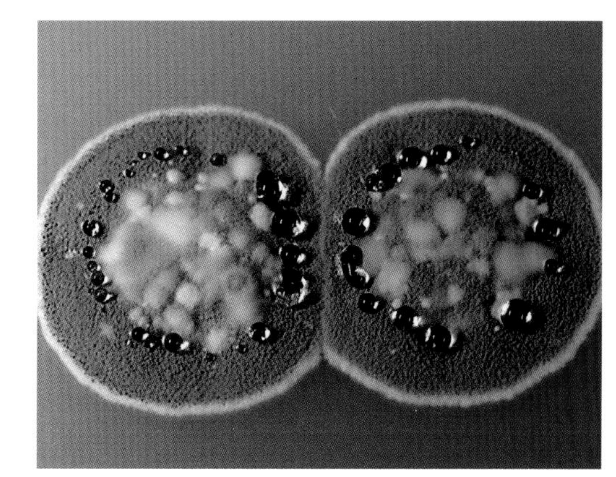

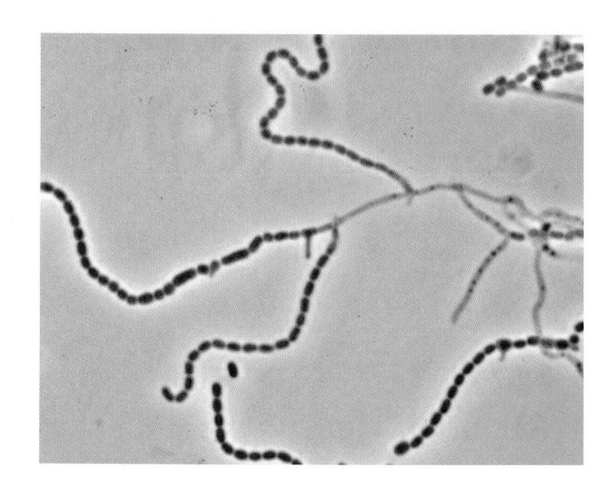

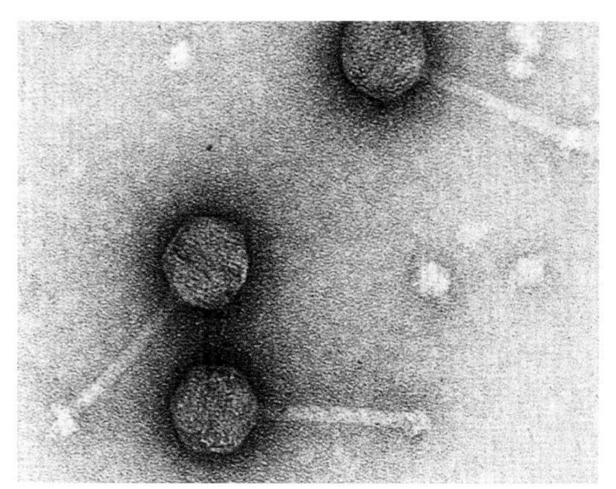

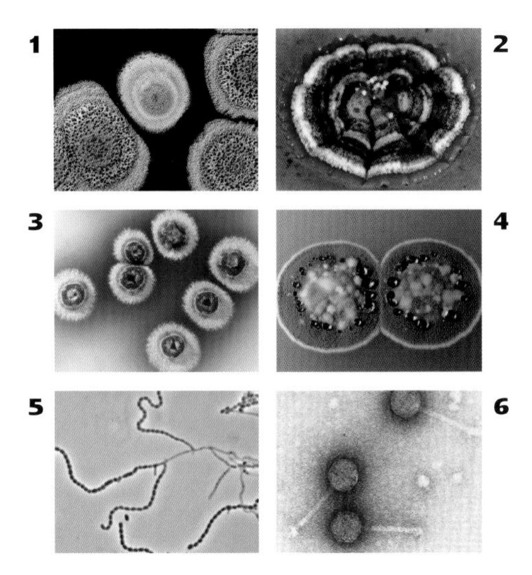

1 Colonies of soil bacteria.
Image: Tobias Kieser.

2 This could be a flower, but really it's a colony of bacteria. The bits sticking up in the middle are not stamens – they are clumps of white spore chains on red stalks made of hundreds of threads held together by a kind of plastic.
Image: Keith Chater.

3 These roughly circular patches are colonies of one kind of soil bacteria. Each colony is about 8 mm across, and contains many millions of cells. It took each colony about four days to grow from a single cell. The bacteria make a blue substance.
Image: Keith Chater.

4 The surface of these colonies does not like water (a bit like a new non-stick frying pan), so the water droplets don't spread out.
Image: Tobias Kieser.

5 Streptomyces spore chains: looking through a normal microscope at one of the water-hating colonies reveals threads from which chains of sausage-like spores have branched. A thousand of these spores end-to-end would stretch for 1 mm!
Image: Keith Chater.

6 Even bacteria get sick! These beautiful objects cause bacteria to become ill. They are viruses, tiny enough for hundreds of them to fit inside a single bacterial cell. That's what happens only about half an hour after one gets in and starts to multiply. Then the cell breaks up and the viruses get out. Each of them can then immediately restart the process in another bacterial cell.
Image: Tim Clayton and Mervyn Bibb.

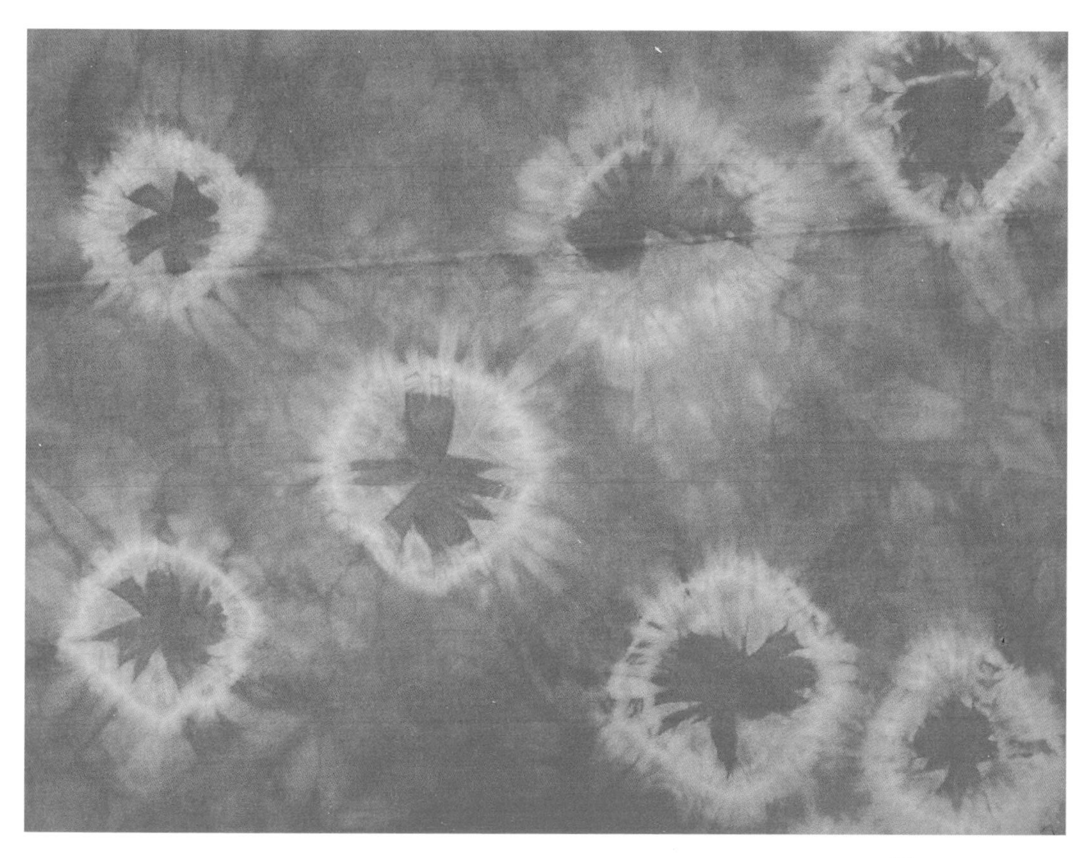

Ellie Brown Age 8

Toxic cake

A nice slice of cake,
just for you,
with yellow and white and pink and blue,
all flimsy and blobby,
glistening in the sun,
but you wouldn't eat it,
it's not like a bun,
it's toxic and horrid,
and terribly bad,
if you ate it you'd die,
now that would be sad.

Alistair Brand Age 9

Blue bacteria

Like a marble cut in half,
blue, black and white,
jewels around a white eyeball,
clouds surrounded by black raindrops,
black marbles sparkling like diamonds,
a pair of binoculars left in the mud,
black circles like aliens,
bouncing around the clouds.

Joseph Burrell Age 9

Laura Flynn Age 7

The death eater

Slimy, creepy, making you jump,
in the night, a scare and a fright,
creeping blue man with a black head,
shining white rhino with a purple horn,
as hard as a brick wall,
as brave as a warrior ready to go to battle,
as hot as a flaming fire,
as big as a mud monster,
as fast as a rollercoaster going down a hill.

Jake Hollis Age 8

The secret world

The secret world,
a sun with eyes,
a dark planet,
a 100 eyed monster,
little planets inside a big one,
lots of shells,
how do you get into the secret world?
A microscope.
If you go to the top you will fall off.

Solomon Ireson Age 8

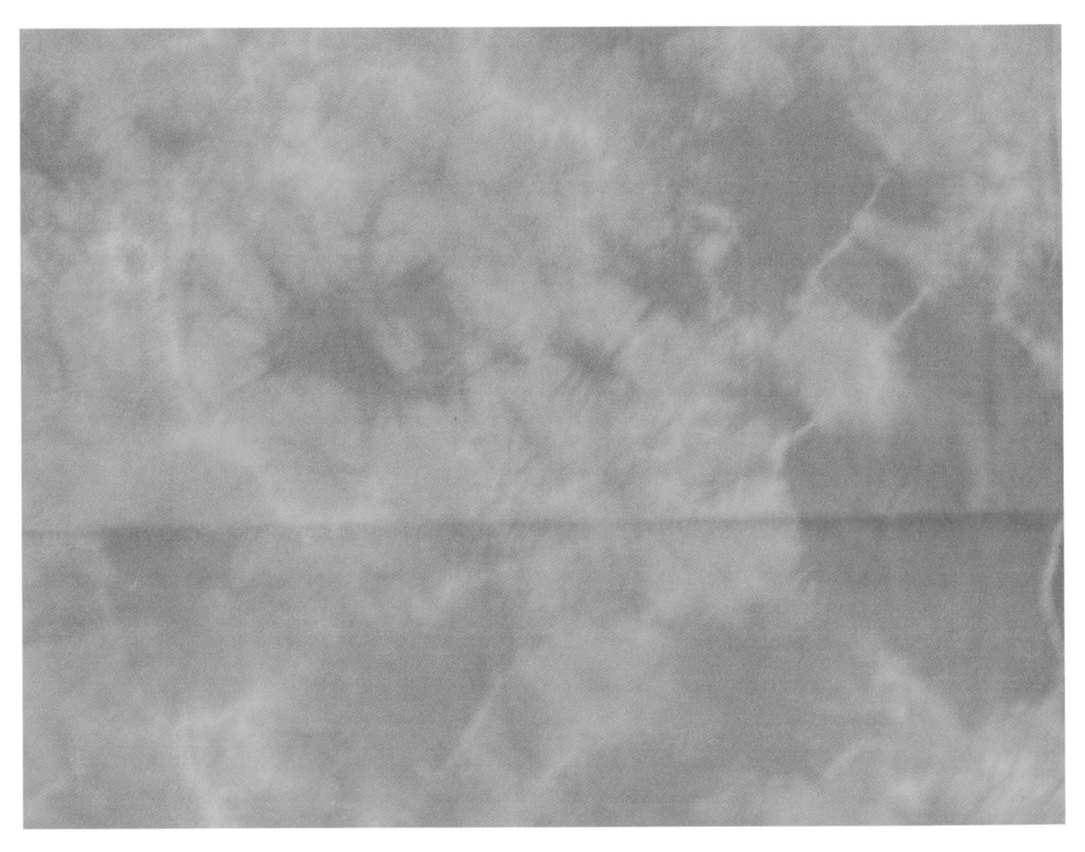

William Ringwood Age 8

Eyes

They're looking, looking,
looking at you.
They can see you in yellow,
they can see you in blue.
They're looking, looking,
looking through eyes.
Scary bacteria in the shape of an eye,
they're looking, looking all the time.

Alistair Brand Age 9

Eyes

Googly eyes,
horrible eyes,
angry eyes,
ugly eyes,
sharp eyes,
pointy eyes,
black in the night eyes,
grey eyes,
staring at me.

Jasmine Smith Age 9

Cheesecake creature

A giant cheesecake creature,
as slimy as can be,
as cold as ice cream,
as bumpy as a rough road,
as squishy as a soft toy,
his name is cheesecake creature.

Lewis Jackson Age 9

Tie-dye drying

Emulsions

Alan Mackie
Institute of Food Research

My main research interests have been in how foams and emulsions are stabilised and the nature of the interactions between systems stabilised by proteins and those stabilised by soap-like surfactants. We have shown that when there are mixtures of protein and surfactant at bubble or droplet surfaces, they can destabilise the system causing bubbles to burst and droplets to merge. More recently I have been interested in how emulsions break down in the gut and specifically how small drops and other particles interact with the thin layer of mucus that protects the surface of the intestine.

emulsions

Tacolneston Primary School

Teacher **Christina Douglas**
Age range of children **7–11**

Scientist **Alan Mackie**
Artist **Chris Hann**
Writer **Martin Figura**

I learned that a bubble had three layers.
I learned how to write a good poem
and to enjoy writing.

Sophie Richardson Age 8

I never knew how interesting a bubble was.

James Anderson Age 8

It was an excellent day.

Tina Douglas Teacher

It was the best day.

Louis Bishop Age 8

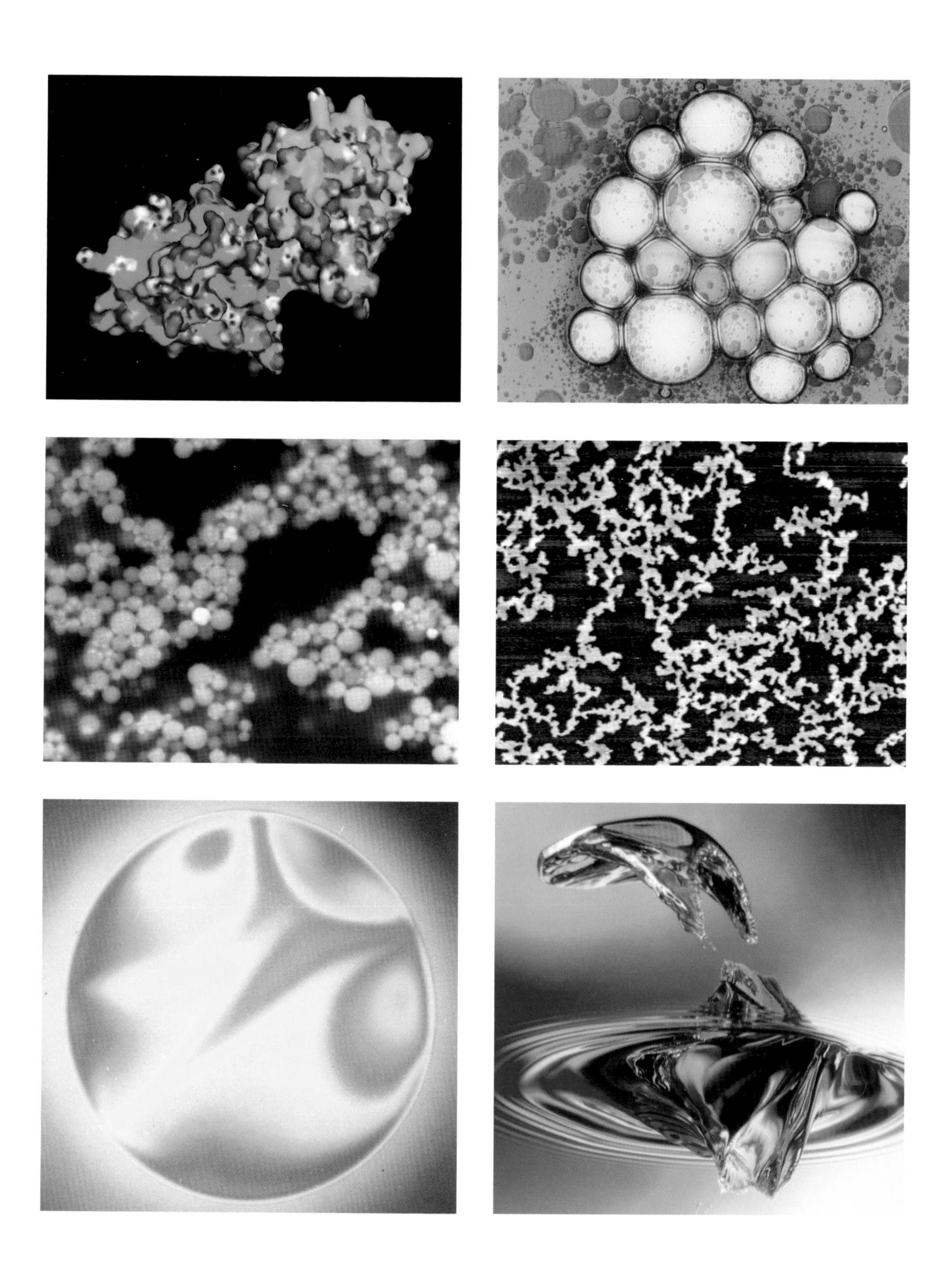

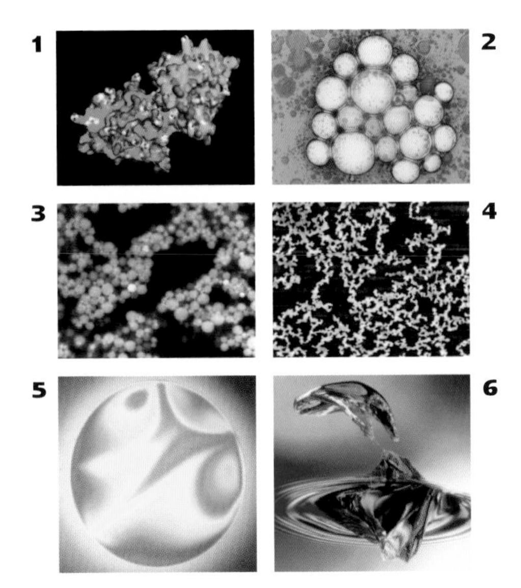

1 This is a computer model of a whey protein from cow's milk called ß-lactoglobulin. The protein forms a dimer (two molecules stuck together), which is shown in green and turquoise. We work with this protein a lot as it is an important food ingredient and has some interesting properties.

Image: Alan Mackie.

2 Physical properties of water (dyed orange), air (white bubbles) and oil (blue background). Bubbles and droplets are important in providing texture and sensation in foods and are often stabilised by proteins such as ß-lactoglobulin.

Image: Jeremy Burgess/Science Photo Library.

3 Flocculated emulsion. When droplets are made in an emulsion, if the force holding them apart is not strong enough, they start to stick together (flocculation) without merging together (coalescence). This can make the liquid emulsion start to gel.

Image: Alan Mackie.

4 A protein film. When there is a mixture of proteins and smaller molecules (surfactants) at an interface they can separate out and form patterns like the one shown. This is an atomic force microscopy (AFM) image of such a film and the bright areas are one molecule thick. This thin protein layer is sitting on a very flat surface (mica) which is the black part.

Image: Alan Mackie.

5 When two drops or bubbles come together they form 'thin films'. It is the behaviour of these films that determines whether the drops or bubbles will merge. The film must be very thin (1/1000th of a millimetre) to show these colours.

Image: Alan Mackie.

6 This is a coin being dropped into water. Water has a high surface tension (skin) which means it takes a lot of energy to make bubbles, especially small ones. Proteins on the surface can lower the surface tension and make it easier to form bubbles.

Image: Dr John Brackenbury/Science Photo Library.

The beautiful bubble

A diamond winding through
a shimmering waterfall.
An elegant ballerina twirling
swirling around
as clear as crystal on display.
An angel, sitting on top of a prickly,
green Christmas tree as it
transforms
its beautiful watery shapes into
soft wings,
flies off into the thick, cool air,
sweeping the dust in its tracks.

Danielle Gibbons Age 8

Verity Knights Age 7

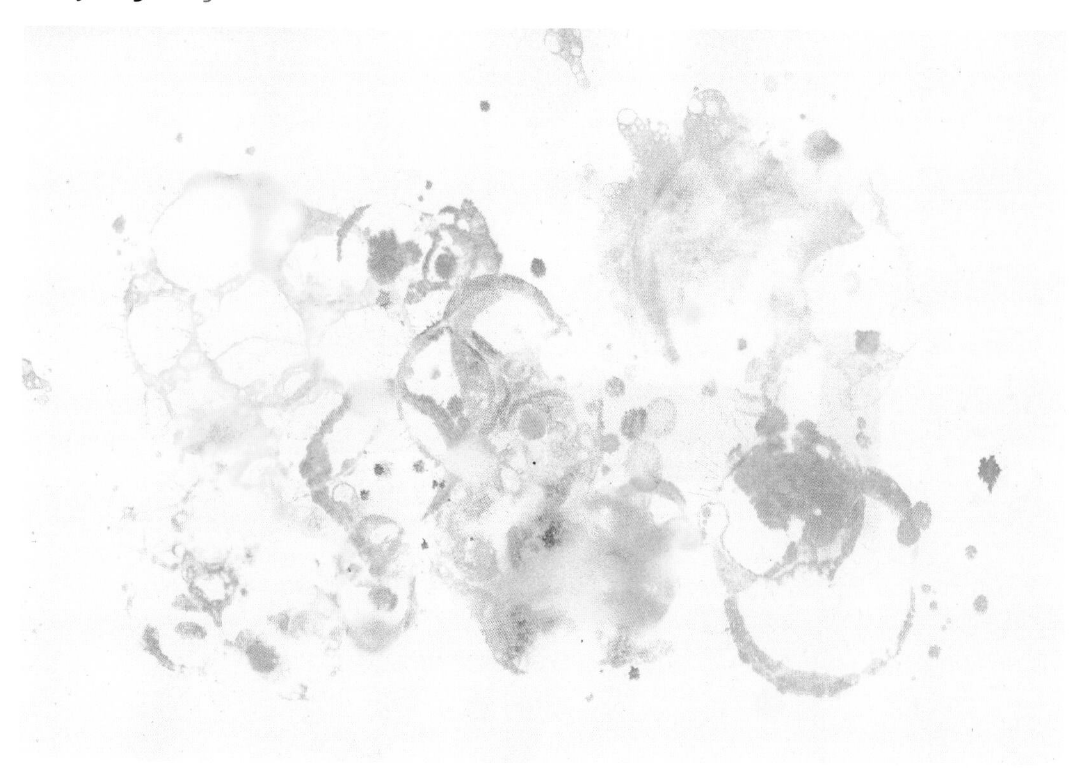

Colourful

Colourful like decorations on the
Christmas tree.
Round bubbles,
soapy, smooth, soft.
Big bubbles.

Jamie Mayes Age 8

Marvellous bubble

The multicoloured patterns
were swirly, dripping
pearls, silky,
soapy, lonely,
sweeping shapes
like tear drops.

Abbie Brown Age 7

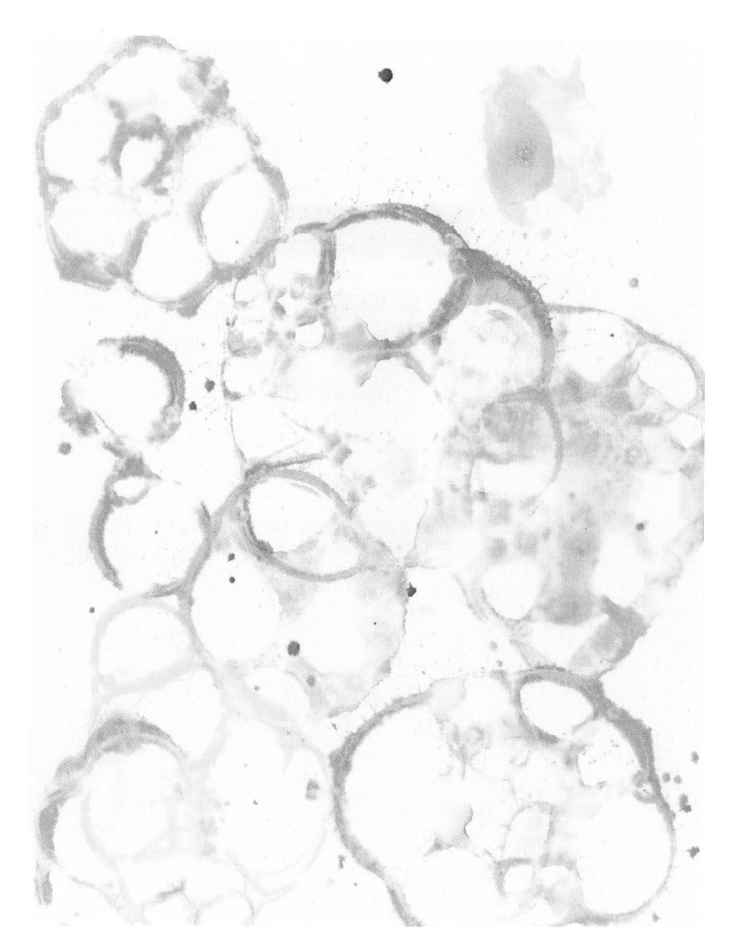

Lydia Brownlow Age 10

Bubble world

A deep smooth colourful world of distinctive
places in me.
A bright oil slick across the air.
An elegant cut in the beautiful eye of the heart.
A diamond swirl of water in the bright light.

Robert Gowing Age 7

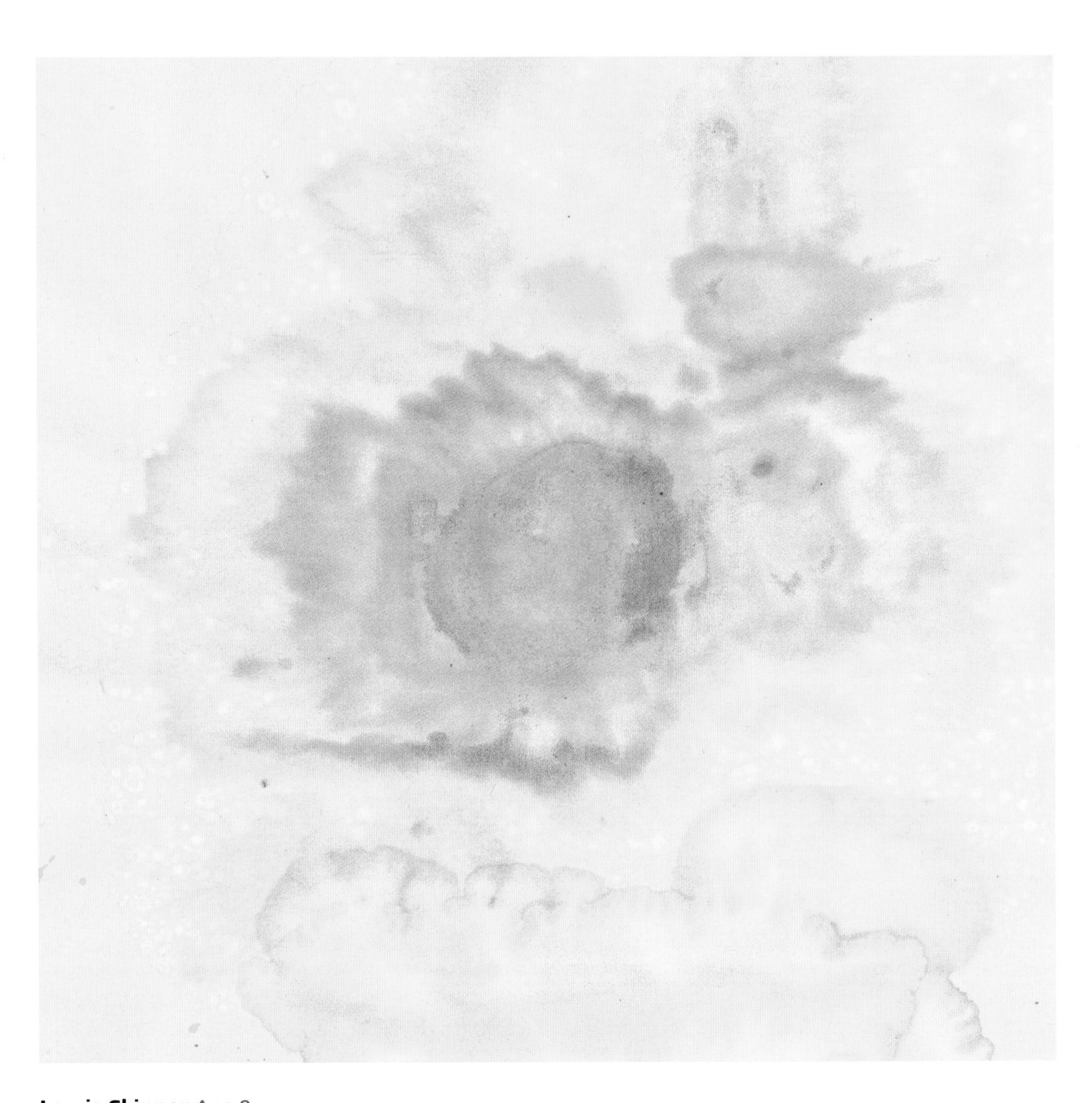

Lewis Skinner Age 9

Salmonella

Vittoria Danino
Institute of Food Research

Salmonella still causes a lot of disease in the UK and the main source of the bacterium is poultry. I am particularly interested in how *Salmonella* infects and survives in chickens and eggs. I am doing this by studying which genes *Salmonella* uses during infection. If we can understand the strategies *Salmonella* uses to contaminate our food, we may become more effective at preventing disease.

Salmonella

North Elmham Primary School

Teacher **Joanna Coe**
Age range of children **9–11**

Scientist **Vittoria Danino**
Artist **Sarah Jarrett**
Writer **Tom Corbett**

All of the children achieved good results and were proud of their work.

Joanna Coe Teacher

All of the lessons inspired me.

Charlotte Walker Age 8

Science is really exciting.

Louisa Scott Age 10

I learned how you get food poisoning.

Harry Jennings Age 9

It was fun and exciting to think of Salmonella *as warriors.*

Megan Ballman Age 11

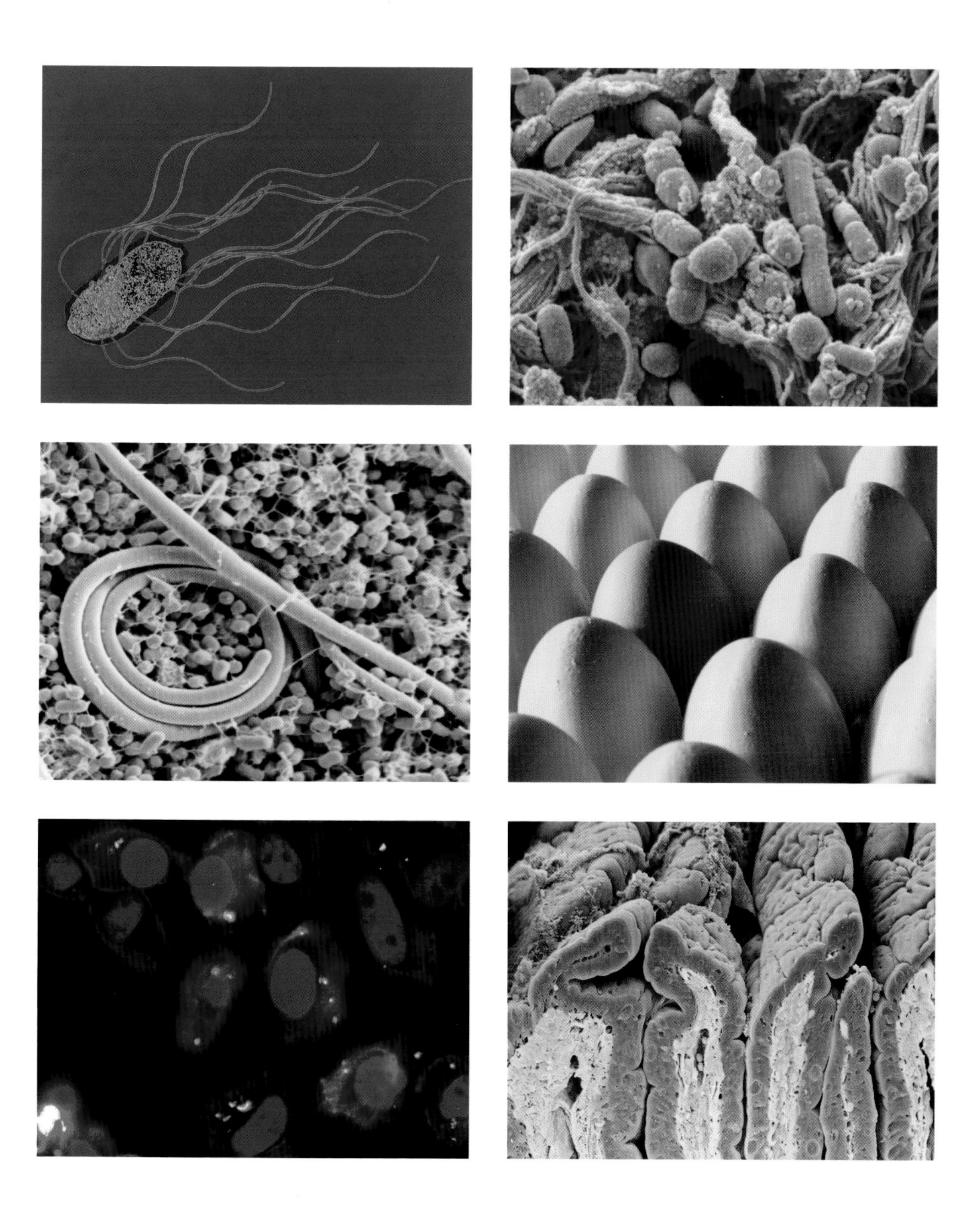

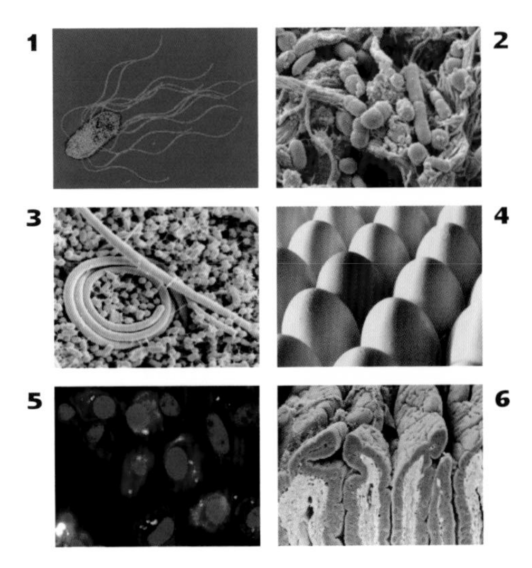

1 *Salmonella* is a rod-shaped bacterium which can swim. *Salmonella* inhabit the human gut and can cause food poisoning and other diseases, such as typhoid fever in humans.

Image: Dr Linda Stannard, UCT/Science Photo Library.

2 Chicken skin contaminated with bacteria, including *Salmonella*.

Image: SCIMAT/Science Photo Library.

3 Cells of *Salmonella enteritidis* change shape as they grow. This scanning electron micrograph (SEM) shows a mixture of small cells and very large cells. Small cells arise only during certain growth stages and efficiently contaminate eggs when the time is right.

Image: Jean Guard-Petter/Science Photo Library.

4 Rows of chicken eggs.

Image: Martin Bond/Science Photo Library.

5 *Salmonella* can enter human cells and kill them. This image shows *Salmonella* (green) inside human cells. The structure of the cell is maintained by a scaffold of actin (red) and the DNA of the cell is stained blue.

Image: Vittoria Danino.

6 Intestinal lining. Coloured scanning electron micrograph (SEM) of the surface of the small intestine. The surface consists of deep folds, called villi. The intestinal surface (top) is exposed to food (pink). Surface cells (red) are supported by connective tissue (light brown) that forms the core of each fold (villus). The folds increase the area for the absorption of nutrients from food.

Image: Steve Gschmeissner/Science Photo Library.

The invasion of Salmonella

Fast twirler
Good darter
Gut invader
Great hurter
Little blighter
Nasty injector
Cell killer
Unstoppable infector
Acid hater
Antibiotic-hater
Vomit maker.

John Luke Hodson Age 11

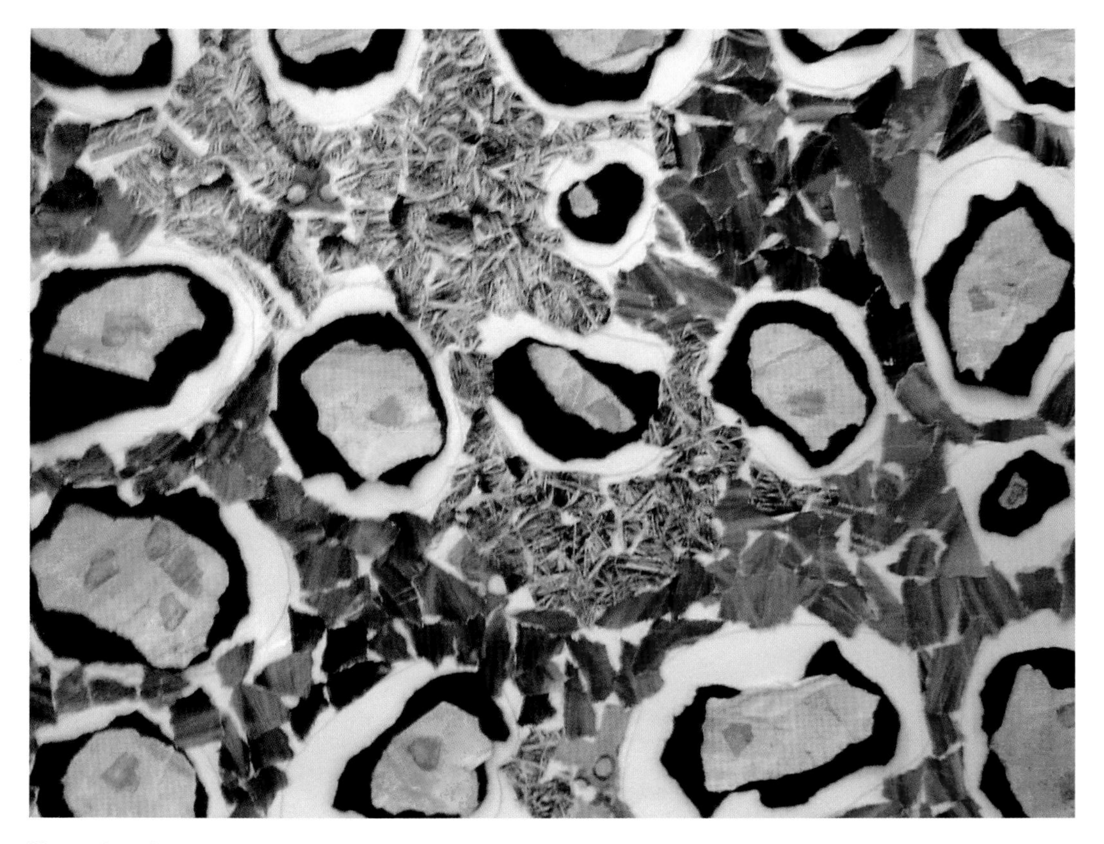

Harry Jennings Age 9

Warriors invade

The warriors hid silently
in the mouldy cabbage leaf
waiting for the victim
to chomp it up with his roast beef.

When he took a bite
the warriors charged,
forming together,
making a barge.

Sailing down the saliva river,
sliding down the throat
to their destination
in their bacteria boat.

Macrophages, white blood cells
standing brave and tall
try to stop the warriors
creating a wall.

The goodies defeated,
the warriors invade,
swimming and celebrating
in some guzzled lemonade.

But they stop abruptly,
no time for play and fun.
They've got to work together
there are jobs to be done!

They make the stomach gurgle,
push through intestines, small,
making diarrhoea,
forming an evil ball.

Out pop the evil slayers
into the loo
making the bathroom smell
because of the stinky poo.

Megan Frances Ballman Age 11

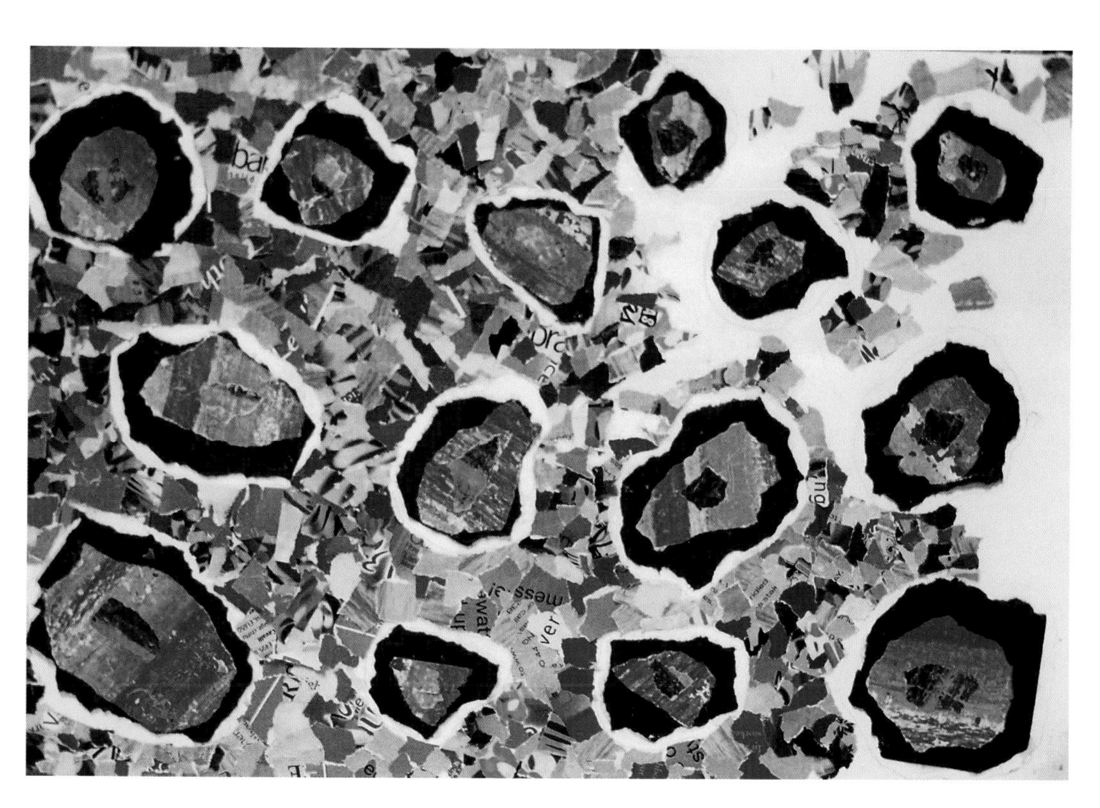

Katie Mayes Age 11

The invaders

whirling!
splashing!
squelching!
hurting!
darting!
laughing!

James Hutcheson Age 10

The invader

Trooping forward, standing to attention,
ready your injection,
skim down the motorway,
left right, left right,
attack!
Squirt squelch, squirt squelch,
inject your poison!

Blood cells, fight back,
release your killer chemicals,
make this war victorious!
Win this land back,
hurry, be quick, they're breeding.

Angus Gregory Holder Age 10

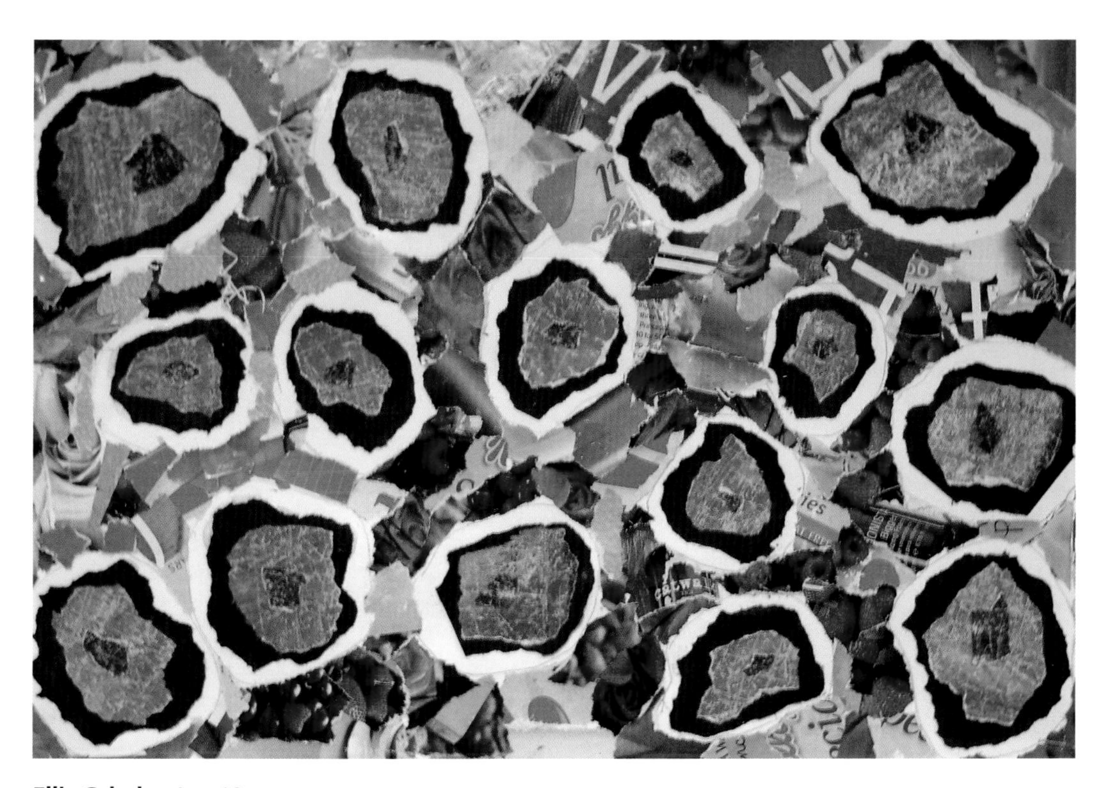

Ellie Scholes Age 10

Invaders

Darting down my soggy throat
scuttling down my complicated organs
slithering down my gooey guts
swimming round the centre of my disgusting stomach
skidding through my slimy body.

George Jarvis Age 10

Starch

Alison Smith
John Innes Centre

Matilda Crumpton-Taylor
John Innes Centre

We study how plants acquire carbon from carbon dioxide in the atmosphere and convert it into sugars and starch. The starch that we study is important as food for humans, but it's also used in a very wide range of industries – as diverse as paper manufacture and crude oil extraction. There's a simple test for the presence of starch, and we used this test in our SAW project to explore which everyday objects and materials contain starch. Starch is not only useful, it's also very beautiful. Although it looks like a powder, in fact it's made up of minute but very intricate granules, with beautiful external and internal structures. In the SAW project we used microscopes to look at starch granules inside living plants. Then we worked with a lot of different close-up photographs and drawings of starch granules as the basis for art and poetry.

starch

Trowse Primary School

Teacher **Clive Portman**
Age range of children **9–11**

Scientists **Alison Smith and Matilda Crumpton-Taylor**
Artist **Sarah Jarrett**
Writer **Tom Corbett**

'SAW' days are an ongoing learning experience for me and I feel that I take away a lot at the end of each day.

Sarah Jarrett Artist

We all found it fun and exciting to see which things had starch in them.

India Bradbury Age 10

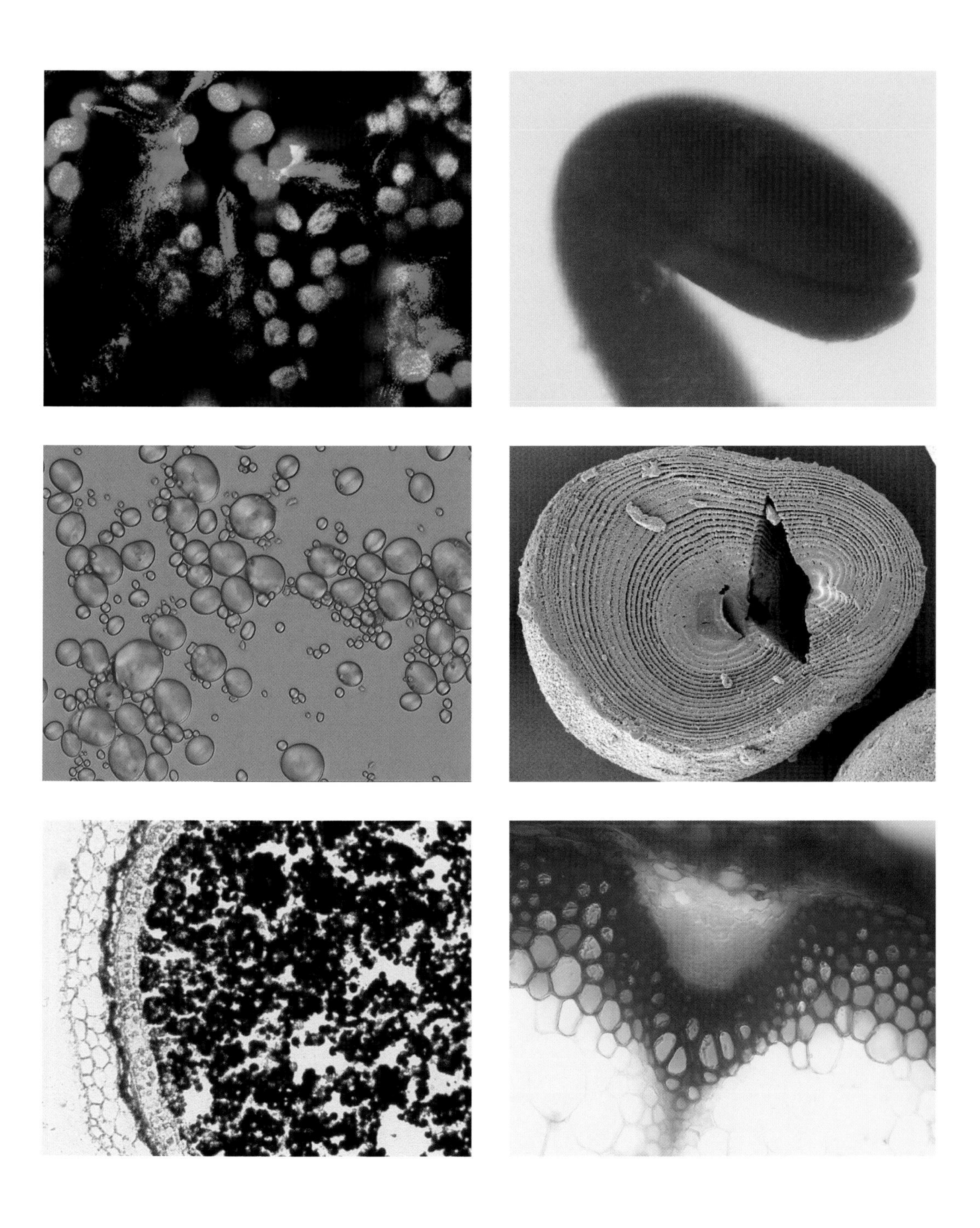

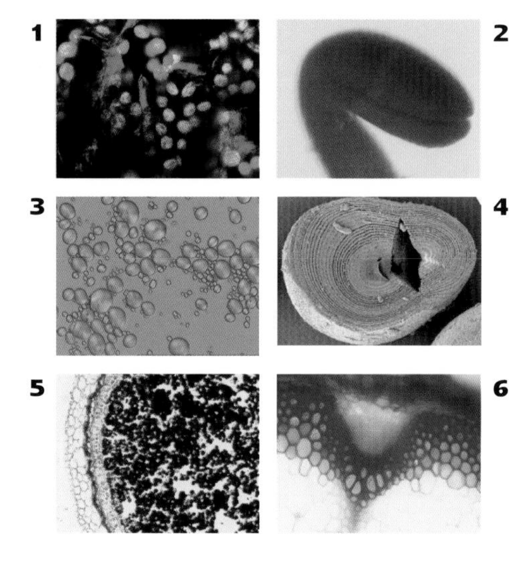

1 A fluorescence microscopy picture of chloroplasts (the red and yellow objects) inside the cells of a leaf.
Image: Sylviane Comparot.

2 The two seed leaves (cotyledons) of the embryo from inside a seed of thale cress (*Arabidopsis*).
Image: Vasilios Andriotis.

3 Starch granules from inside a potato tuber, seen under polarised light.
Image: Alison Smith

4 A single starch granule from a potato tuber, cracked open to show the 'growth rings' inside.
Image: Emma Pilling.

5 The picture shows the edge of a slice through a grain of barley. The dark material consists of tightly packed starch granules inside the grain: the dark colour results from the staining of the granules with iodine.
Image: Alison Smith.

6 Part of a section through a plant stem, stained to show the walls of the cells. These thick cell walls support and strengthen the stem.
Image: Paul Derbyshire.

Carp

Open the lid.
What do you see?
Black slimy bugs
running, scurrying, bumping
in the box.

Feed them starch.
What do you see?
Dark inky black carp
growing, growing
big as a giant jelly baby.

Lucy Aitken Age 9

My picture looks like a fossil

The one in my picture is huge,
but it's small in reality
it has starch in
it is complicated
but I know what it means.

Franceska Bailey Madden Age 9

Clocks

Crowding together resembling clocks,
Loud and clearly ticking and tocking.
On and off the rhythm went.
Clocks all shapes and sizes.
Key parts of the clock never stopped.
Skinny hands turned round and round.

Jack Wason Age 11

Shells

Staying on the dry yellow beach,
hearing something I always hear,
enormous crabs leave me,
letting small crabs live in me,
looking at the aqua sea,
seeing children and adults around me.

Chey Veal Age 9

Plant natural products

Sam Mugford
John Innes Centre

Melissa Dokarry
John Innes Centre

Sam Mugford and Melissa Dokarry investigate how and why different plants make different kinds of natural products – the chemicals that we associate with the tastes, colours and flavours of different plant species and that, in some cases, are extracted for medicinal use and for other commercial purposes. Melissa is a PhD student and is investigating the structures of the enzymes that synthesise particular natural products, through computer modelling and X-ray crystallography. Sam, a postdoctoral scientist, is investigating the biochemical function of these enzymes, and is also looking into the role of plant natural products in interactions between plants and other organisms. Melissa and Sam both work in Anne Osbourn's lab at the John Innes Centre.

Martham Primary School

Teacher **Heather Delf**
Age range of children **7–9**

Scientists **Sam Mugford and Melissa Dokarry**
Artist **Chris Hann**
Writers **Mike O'Driscoll and Joe Mugford**

We did lots of inventing.

Xena Dyball Age 9

I found out how to make an atom structure and paint it.

Joe Smith Age 9

I liked extracting coloured chemicals from plants.

Sophie Windsor Age 9

The images were intriguing and highly colourful and inspired the imaginations of the children.

Heather Delf Teacher

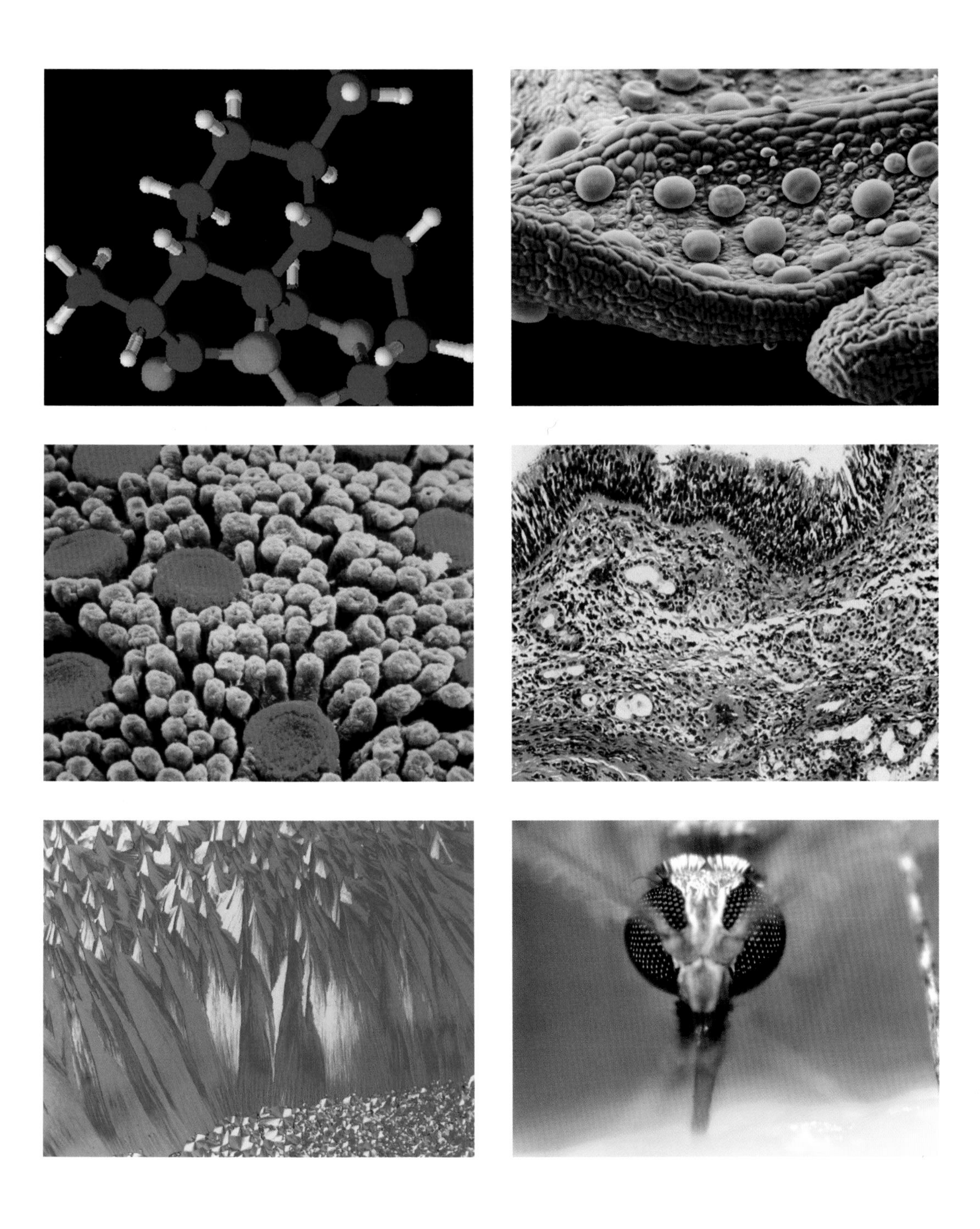

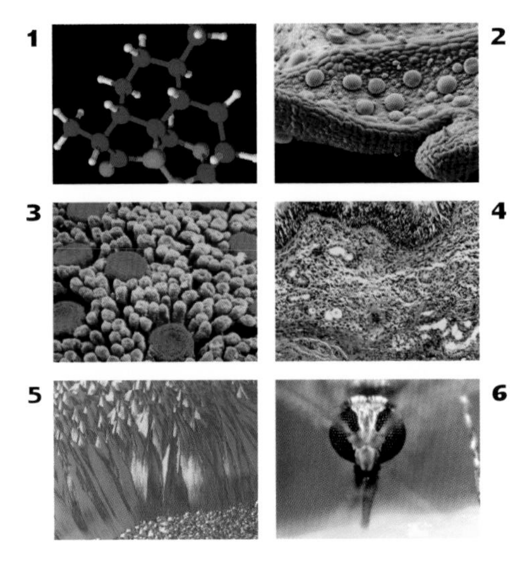

1 Artemisinin. This shows the structure of the antimalarial drug artemisinin, or Qinghaosu as it is known in China where it was discovered. This compound is made by the sweet wormwood plant (*Artemisia annua*).
Image: Sam Mugford.

2 The surface of a mint leaf showing the trichomes, specialised cells which store the chemicals that give mint its smell and taste.
Image: Eye of Science/Science Photo Library.

3 The surface of a human tongue. The large circular things are the tops of the taste buds, through which we can taste chemicals.
Image: Omikron/Science Photo Library.

4 Nose skin. This is the skin on the inside of a nostril. At the top are the cells that sense the chemicals, like the taste buds do in the mouth. Below, in blue, are the blood vessels that feed these cells, and the nerves that send the information to the brain.
Image: Astrid Kage/Science Photo Library.

5 Polarized light micrograph of crystals of taxol, an important anti-cancer drug found in the bark of yew trees.
Image: Michael W. Davidson/Science Photo Library.

6 An aphid feeding on a leaf. Many plants make chemicals that provide protection against attack by aphids.
Image: Volker Steger/Science Photo Library.

Plant science

Leaves with millions of molecules
fighting plant-eating bugs.
Multi-coloured petals wave
at the tips of long, thin stems.
Bright yellow pollen is collected
by busy, buzzing bees.
Spotted red ladybugs
drift through the air.
Bright petals spring forth
like a Jack-in-a-box.
Lovely purple lavender
fills the air with a colourful scent.

Xena Dyball Age 9

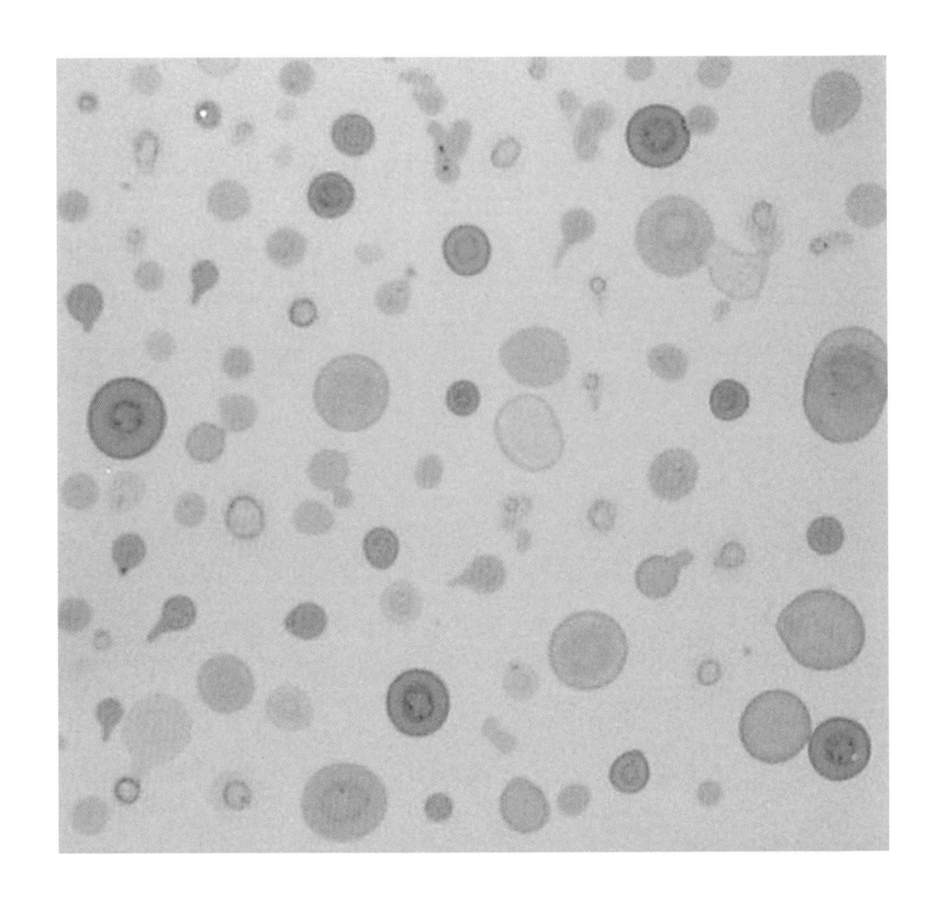

A crowd of people looking up to the sky

A crowd of people in a restaurant,
waiting for their food.
Strawberries, tomatoes, spaghetti bolognaise.
Red icicles, like fruit sweets,
squidgy and gooey like marshmallows and peas.
Bright pink coral under the sea.
People with their tongues hanging out,
tasty, microscopic molecules
drowning in a whirlpool of flavours.

Darcie Lines Age 8

The mosquito

Bulging eyes with a multitude of visions
form a complex compound kaleidoscope.
Thorax as round as footballs,
eyes pitted like golf balls.
Proboscis dangling loosely,
like baubles on a Christmas tree.

Kitty Hawkins Age 8

Science nose

As I crush the molecules with my fingers
cells explode like a bomb.
Chemicals zoom upwards into my nostrils.
Strange smells make my brain dance.

Lloyd Sayer Age 8

Spreading colours

Colourful flames, the light looks alive,
spreading slowly across the paper.
Multi-coloured molecules,
chemicals mixing together,
sparkling in the light,
dancing in the alcohol.

Olivia Hesseltine Age 7

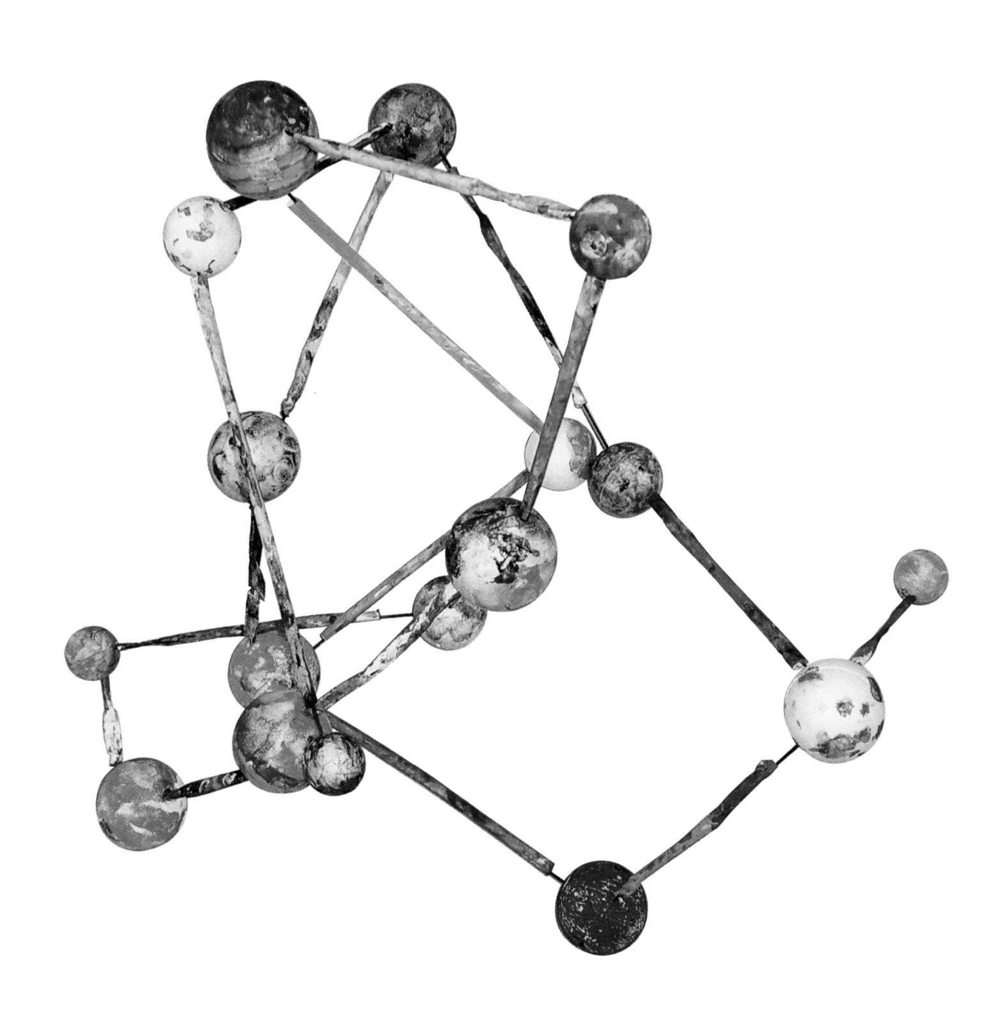

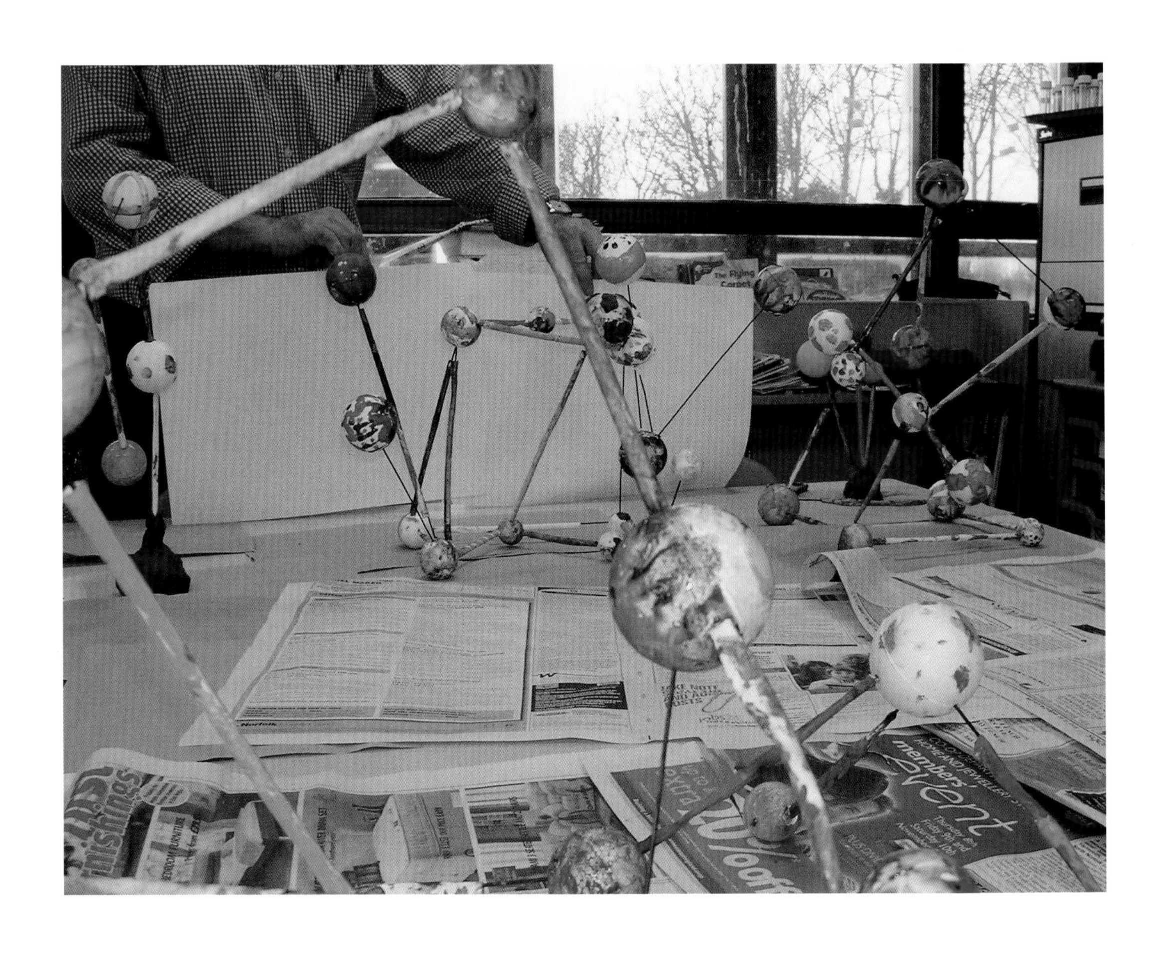
The Flying
members'

Rhizobia

Allan Downie
John Innes Centre

I am interested in how *Rhizobium* bacteria and legume plants communicate to each other when they establish a symbiotic interaction that enables the bacteria to capture nitrogen gas and convert it into a form (ammonia) that can then be used by the plant. This allows leguminous plants (such as peas and beans) to grow without any added nitrogenous fertilizer. My research has focused on how the rhizobia activate a plant-signalling pathway that induces the development of the 'nodules', in which the bacteria convert the nitrogen to ammonia. In the SAW project I focused firstly on the fact that photosynthesis produces sugars which are moved from the leaves to the roots and nodules (via the phloem). I then talked about how the nitrogen compounds produced in the nodules are moved up to the leaves via the xylem, which also moves water up to the leaves. I then explained how the bacteria grow into the root and nodules via specialised tunnels called infection threads. I drew the analogy that the bacteria were a bit like miners going down into a pit where they had to work, but instead of digging coal, the work they had to do was to break the very strong bonds that join two nitrogen atoms together in nitrogen gas. Once the bonds are broken the resulting ammonia (NH_3) is captured by the plant cells and moved up via the xylem to the leaves where it is needed for growth.

rhizobia

Kenninghall Primary School

Teacher **Jan Hewitt**
Age range of children **9–11**

Scientist **Allan Downie**
Artist **Julia Sorrell**
Writer **Tom Corbett**
Musician **Geoff Sharkey**

The project worked very well and gave the children something to remember.

Geoff Sharkey Musician

Responses from children age 9–11:

It was great thinking about what the images meant… such as the nodules… like cows' udders.

Our imaginations could go wild.

Before the project I wasn't interested in roots, but this project has definitely changed my mind.

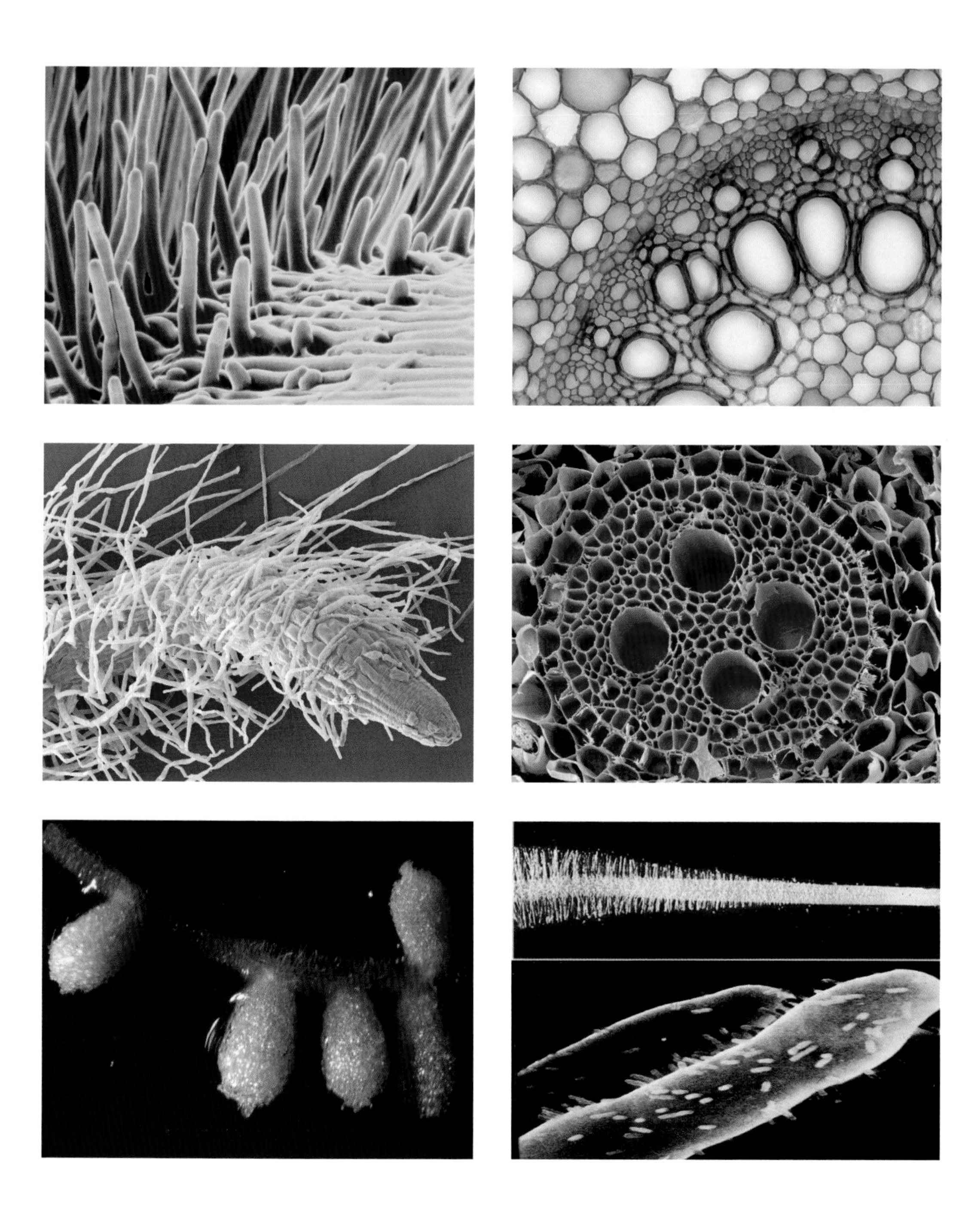

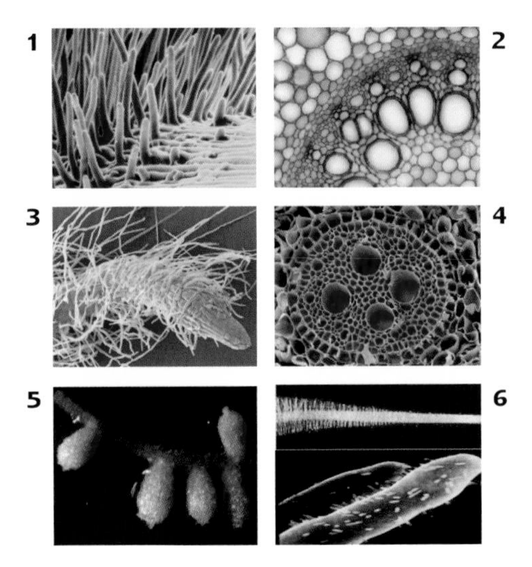

1 Coloured scanning electron micrograph (SEM) of root hairs on a cress root. Root hairs are in intimate contact with soil particles, and enormously increase the root's absorbing surface area. The Cress family (*Cruciferae*) include important vegetables such as turnip, cabbage, cauliflower, radish, watercress and mustard.
Image: Microfield Scientific Ltd./ Science Photo Library.

2 Light micrograph of a section through the central part of the root of an asparagus plant (*Asparagus officinalis*). The root contains vascular tissues, xylem (large blue areas) and phloem (smaller red vessels). Xylem is responsible for carrying water from the roots upwards to the rest of the plant. Phloem transports sugars between the plant's tissues, depending on where they are needed. Outside the vascular region are supporting cortex cells (pink, upper left).
Image: Herve Conge, ISM/ Science Photo Library.

3 SEM of the root of a young poppy seedling. The numerous root hairs (yellow) increase the surface area of the root to maximise uptake of water and nutrients. At the very tip of the root is a hairless root cap which protects the root. Just above this is the apical meristem, an area of rapidly dividing cells where most growth takes place.
Image: Steve Gschmeissner/ Science Photo Library.

4 SEM of a section through a vascular bundle from a rootlet of a dicotyledon plant showing the xylem (orange) and phloem (pink). Surrounding the vascular bundle is a single layer of endodermis (purple) and then cortex (brown), which consists of parenchyma cells.
Image: Steve Gschmeissner/ Science Photo Library.

5 Nodules on a pea root.
Image: Allan Downie.

6 Root and root hairs.
Image: Allan Downie.

In the root mine

Mine! Mine! Mine!
Break the nitrogen
help the plant get the sugar
stay alive! Get to the front
be the winner!
Work! Work! Work!
Multiply - fat, thin
all different shapes.
Be one of the group -
don't let go, hold on.
Eat! Eat! Eat!
Eat the sugar keep healthy
and strong keep the
plant alive make him
reward us for our
brilliance. Enlarge
him, make him grow, work
to death if you have to.
Do your best - make
the master happy!

Dennis Egan Age 10

Dennis Egan Age 10

Bacteria in the mine

Roots reaching, spreading, feeling –
bursting, squirming in heaven
dead, rising, collapsing to the
underworld – resting charging up.
Got to get up, digging.

A BURST OF ENERGY!!!!

Others relying on them,
tunnels leading to safety,
feeding, petrified, poisoned
snake venom iced to the spot.

Eddie Stolash Age 10

Ailsa Warwick Age 9

Underground

Bees mmm mmm mmm –
Hurrying hurrying.
Sugar falling like boulders
rushing to the roots.
Water gushing up the pipes
up and down; up and down.
Roots fighting for the water
stretching, spreading out –
meshing, clashing.

Daniel Hall Age 10

Phloem

Bees going up; workers coming down,
plants growing up –
root going down.
Sugar going down ... shshsh ...
The gushing of the water along the path,
the roots, spreading around like a race.
The bacteria feeding them as fast as they can –
faster, faster!
Plant growing up.
Root growing down.
Bang, bang, crash, bacteria working – hard as they can.

Rees Eagle Age 9

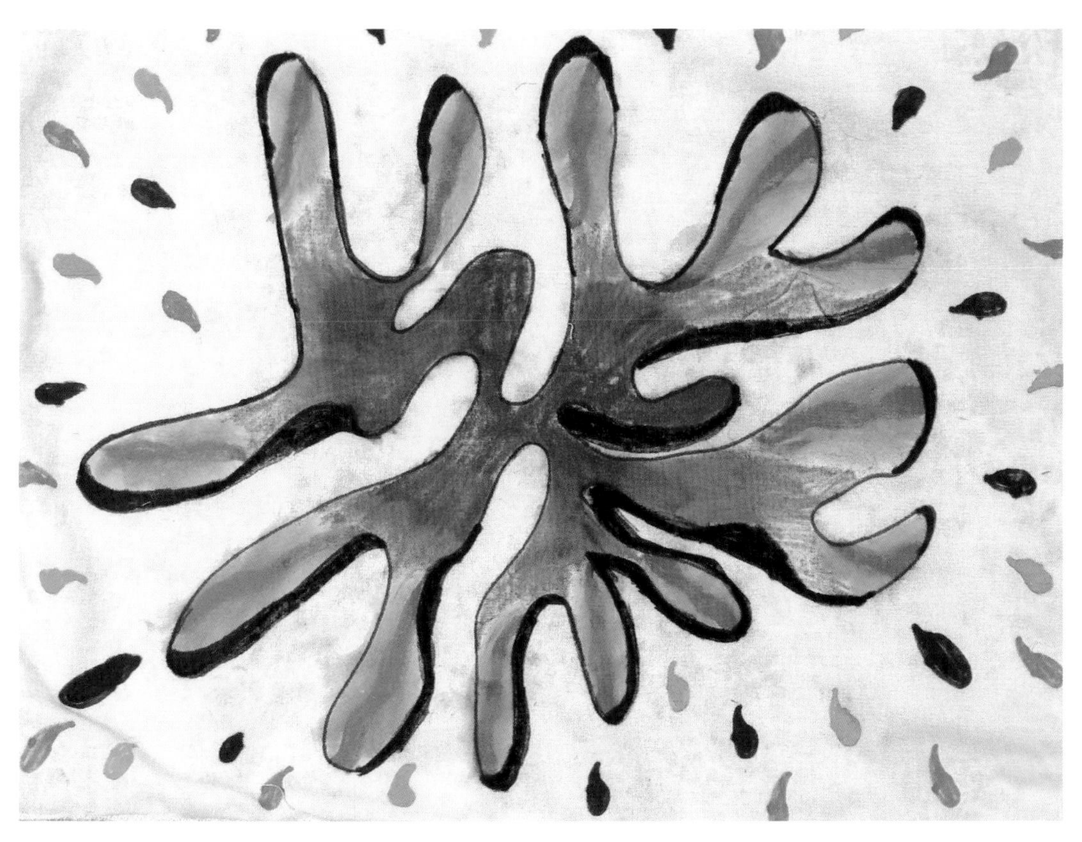

Ben Common Age 10

The world below

A seed,
one seed,
it has to work fast,
really, really fast,
I watch from a distance as the seed begins to grow.

A root,
one root,
it is growing,
the bacteria is here,
I wait for the war to begin.

A war,
one war,
is beginning to start,
the noise is big,
the bacteria are fighting and I sit back and watch.

It stops,
just stops,
it is all over,
the lucky ones are in,
all I can do is watch.

The sugar,
sweet sugar,
is feeding hungry cells,
they are all full,
the work is about to begin.

The water,
life-giving water,
it's going up!
up, up and out of the soil,
it is all over – the plant grows.

The plant,
young plant,
it is dying all alone,
the bacteria are worried,
I watch the sad sight as I hear the helpless cries.

It's over,
all over,
they are dead,
all inside are dead,
the plant and the bacteria are gone.

Georgia Precious Age 11

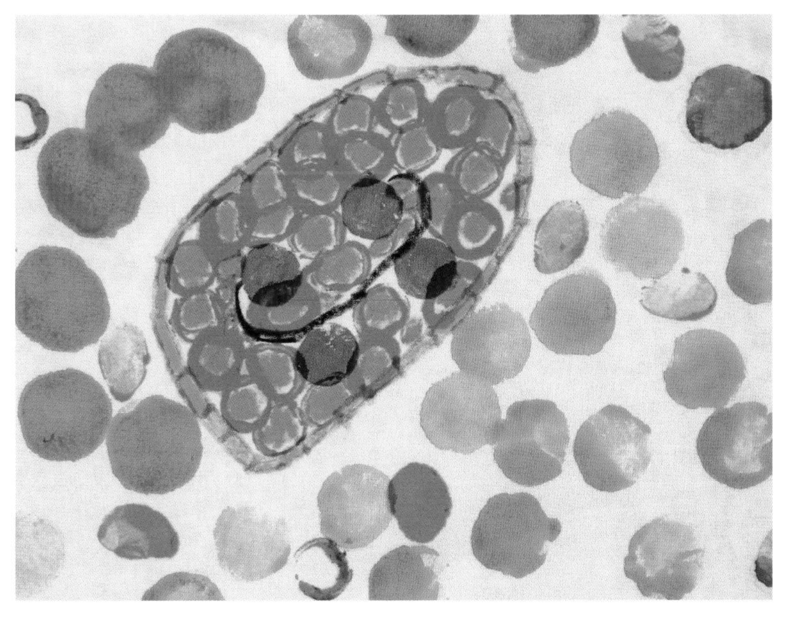

James Knight Age 9

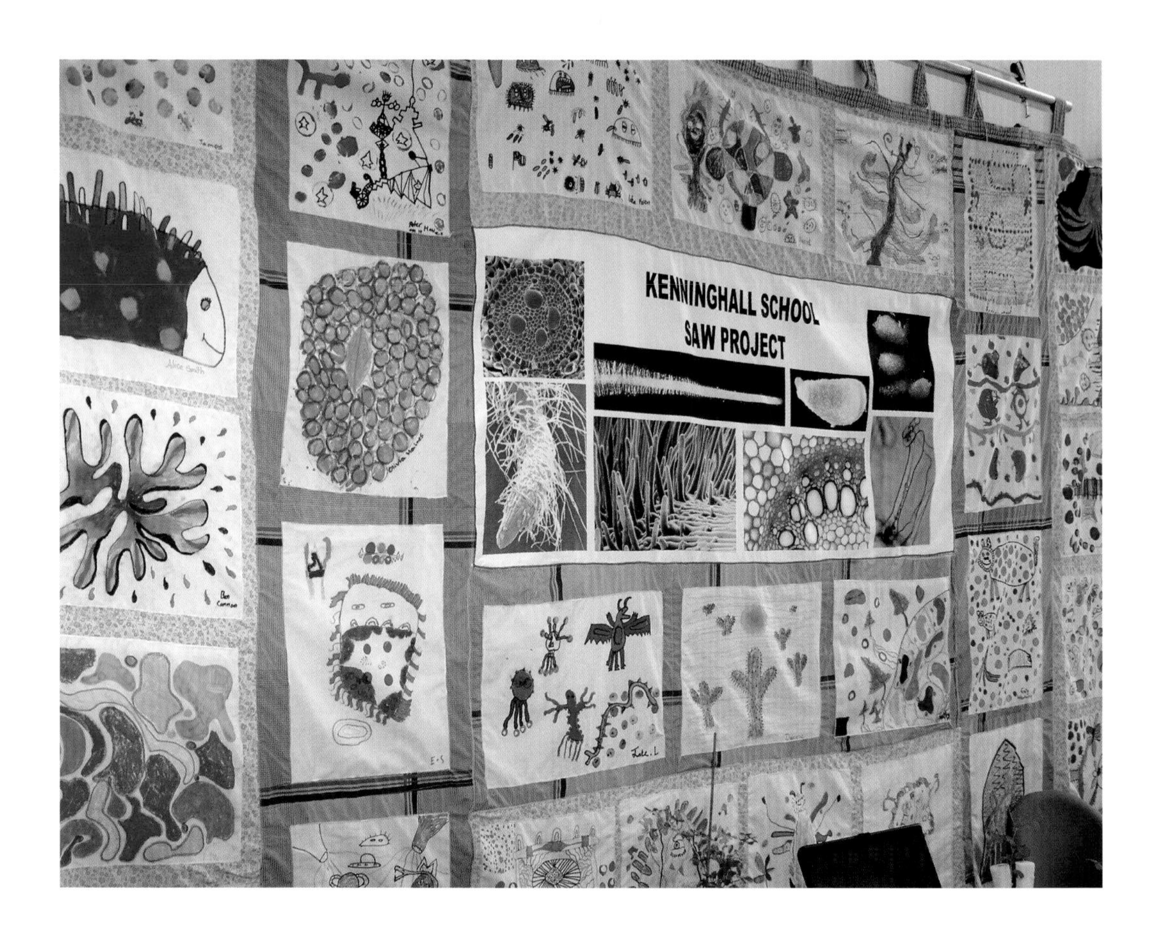
KENNINGHALL SCHOOL
SAW PROJECT

Topoisomerases

Tony Maxwell
John Innes Centre

My research interests concern DNA topoisomerases, enzymes whose job it is to prevent DNA from becoming entangled. These enzymes are also important as targets for drugs, and work in my lab is also aimed at developing new antibiotics.

topoisomerases

Spooner Row Primary School

Teacher **Simon Wakeman**
Age range of children **7–11**

Scientist **Tony Maxwell**
Artist **Chris Hann**
Writer **Mike O'Driscoll**

I enjoyed the day hugely.

Tony Maxwell Scientist

The children were enthralled and very positive about the activities.

Isabel Smith Teacher

I learned that if you mix washing-up liquid with salt and shredded onion and a dash of alcohol you can get DNA. Also I learned that Tony can't spell deoxyribonucleic acid.

Ellie Payne Age 10

I learned that I can write poems and that anything can inspire anything.

Byron Chapman Woods Age 11

My best school day ever!

Megan Welton Age 11

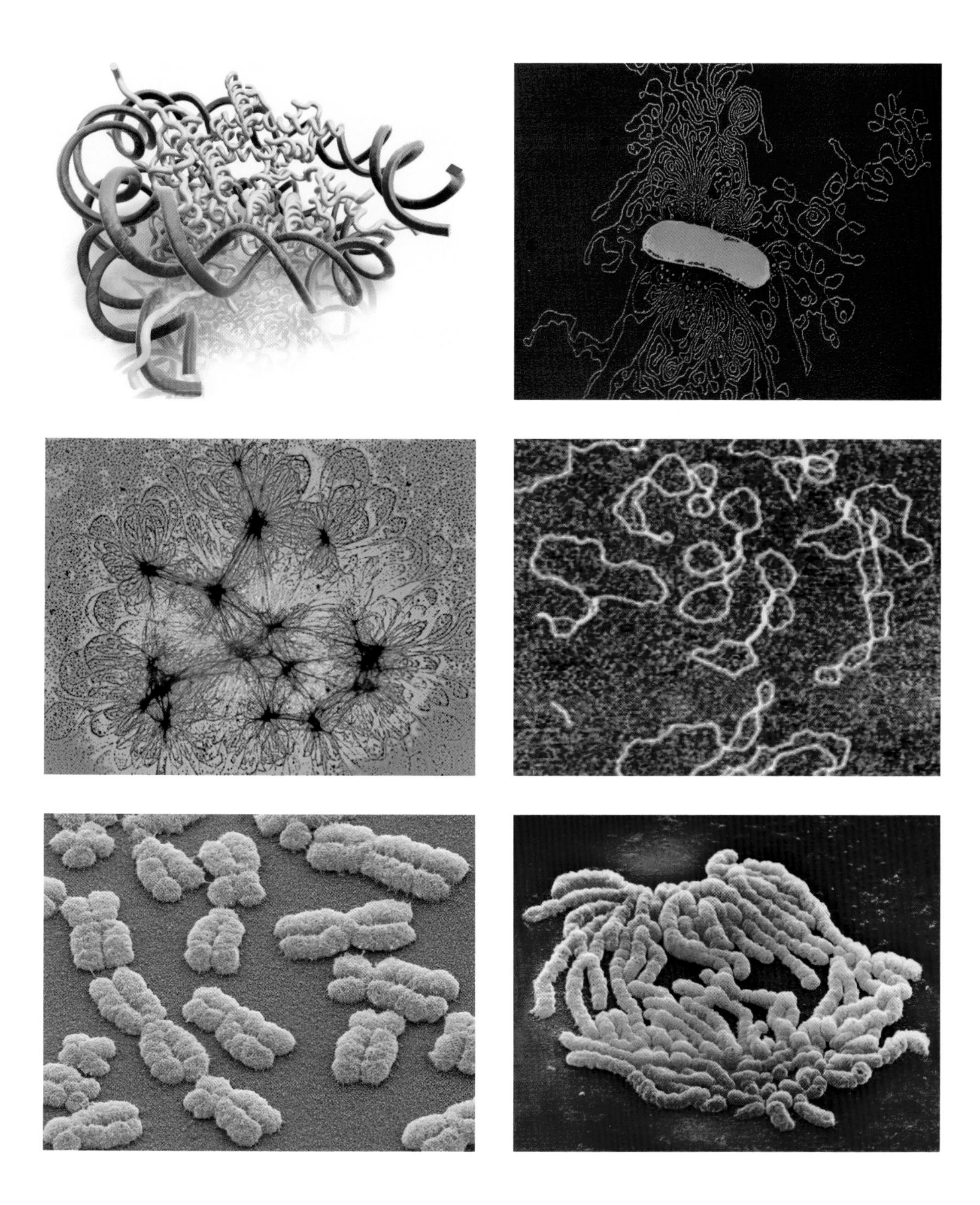

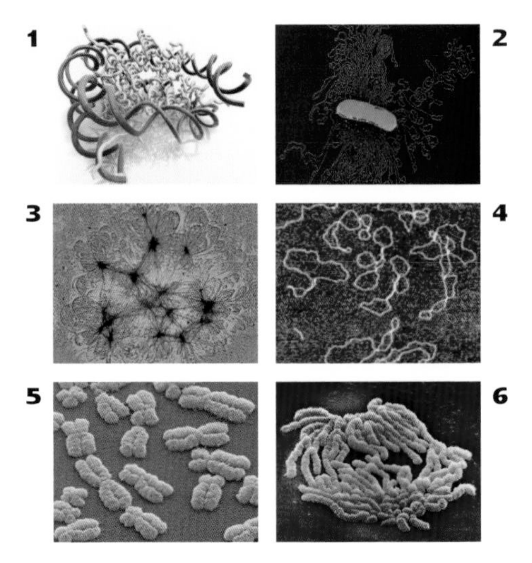

1 Nucleosome, computer artwork. A nucleosome forms part of chromosomes and consists of a short length of DNA (pink and blue) wrapped around a core of proteins (yellow). This structure allows large quantities of DNA to be packaged into a cell's nucleus.
Image: Phantomix/Science Photo Library.

2 *E. coli* DNA. False-colour transmission electron micrograph (TEM) of the bacterium *E. coli* (*Escherichia coli*) surrounded by its DNA. The bacterium was burst open causing its DNA to be ejected. The DNA is visible as the gold-coloured fibrous mass lying around the orange bacterial shell. The total length of DNA is 1.5 mm, 1000 times the length of the bacterium.
Image: Dr Gopal Murti/Science Photo Library.

3 *E. coli* DNA (TEM). Coloured transmission electron micrograph (TEM) of a relaxed DNA molecule (pink) in the bacterium E. coli. Bacteria have a very simple cell structure. Their DNA exists as a naked molecule within the cell's cytoplasm. The majority of the DNA forms one molecule known as the nucleoid (pink).
Image: Dr Elena Kiseleva/Science Photo Library.

4 Drug-DNA complexes. Coloured atomic force micrograph (AFM) of plasmids (loops of DNA found in some bacteria; blue) bound to the anti-cancer drug ditercalinium. This drug distorts the shape of DNA, which eventually causes the death of affected cells. Distorted regions are yellow here.
Image: Torunn Berge/Science Photo Library.

5 Human chromosomes. Coloured scanning electron micrograph (SEM) of pairs of human chromosomes. They consist of genetic material DNA in association with proteins. Most human cells contain 46 chromosomes, 23 inherited from the mother and 23 from the father.
Image: Andrew Syred/Science Photo Library.

6 Meiosis. Coloured scanning electron micrograph (SEM) of chromosomes during anaphase of meiosis (gamete formation). Chromosomes consist of DNA and proteins. Meiosis occurs only in the sex cells (gametes) of the testes and ovaries.
Image: Adrian T Sumner/Science Photo Library.

pink
fluffy
slippers
running
away,
away
to
find
somewhere
else
to
stay
.
running
away
from
the
slipper
man
with
a
frying
pan
.
over
a
ditch
and
thru
a
football
pitch
round
and
round
they
go!

Sam Hewitson Age 7

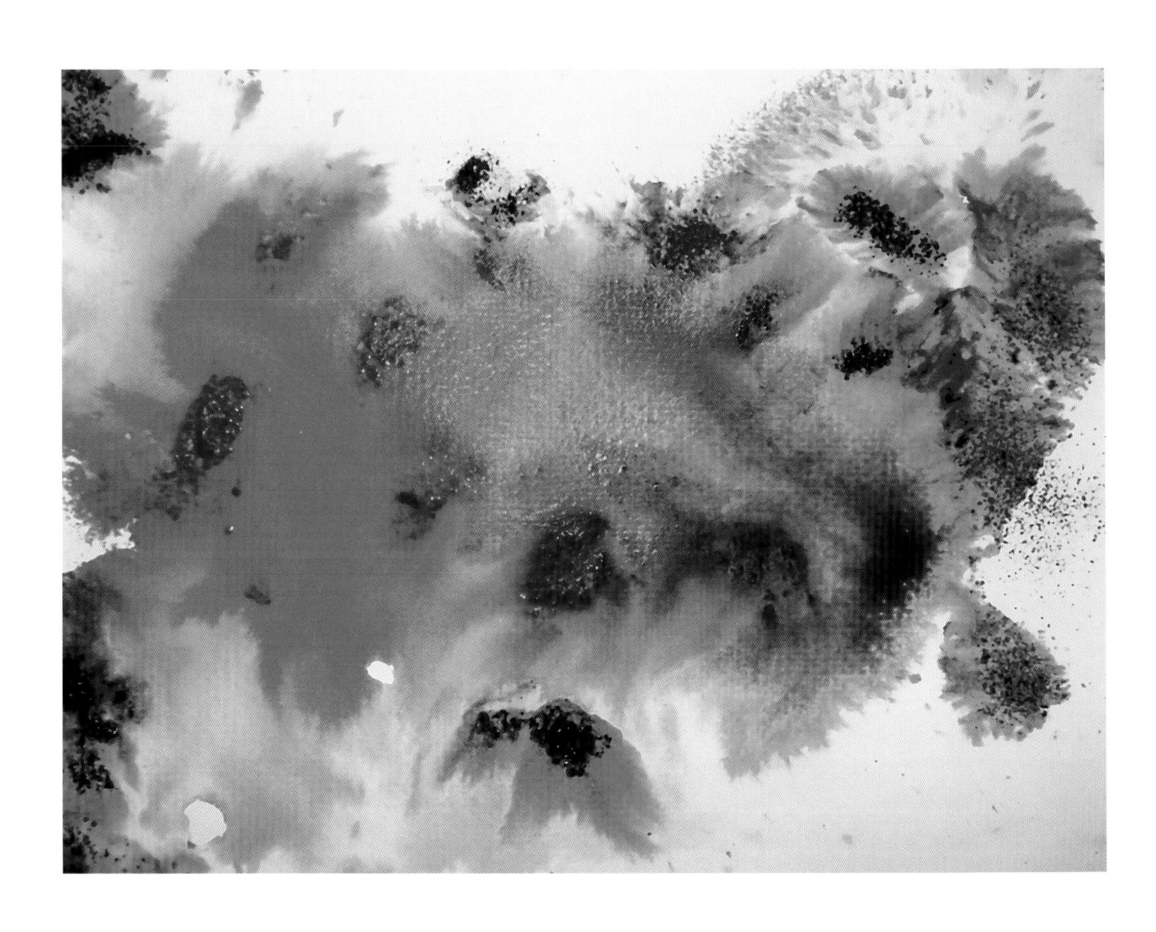

My exploding flowers

I brought some little flowers that grew
and grew and grew and when they were as big
as me they exploded into fireworks.
They flew up in the sky so high and fell
down like little jewels.

Elsa Taylor Age 7

Pink flowers

Pink flowers
exploding
into the high sky.
The pictures of dots
look like chickenpox.

Emily Bristow Age 7

The crowd

Swirling and curling
whirring and stirring.

A necklace a pancake
a sausage a cloud
spaghetti a DNA crowd.

It's your choice.
Go on say it aloud

OR

Bacteria having a pout
and throwing the DNA out

DEOXYRIBO
NUCLEIC
ACID

is really hard to say
so that's why we tone it down
and call it DNA.

Byron Chapman Woods Age 11

DNA

DNA is like flowers exploding,
then flying through the air,

shooting from the wallpaper, like
fireworks zooming into the night
sky,

bursting with colour splatted onto
a green landscape,

just like webs sprawling across
the paper.

Rosie Rackham Age 9

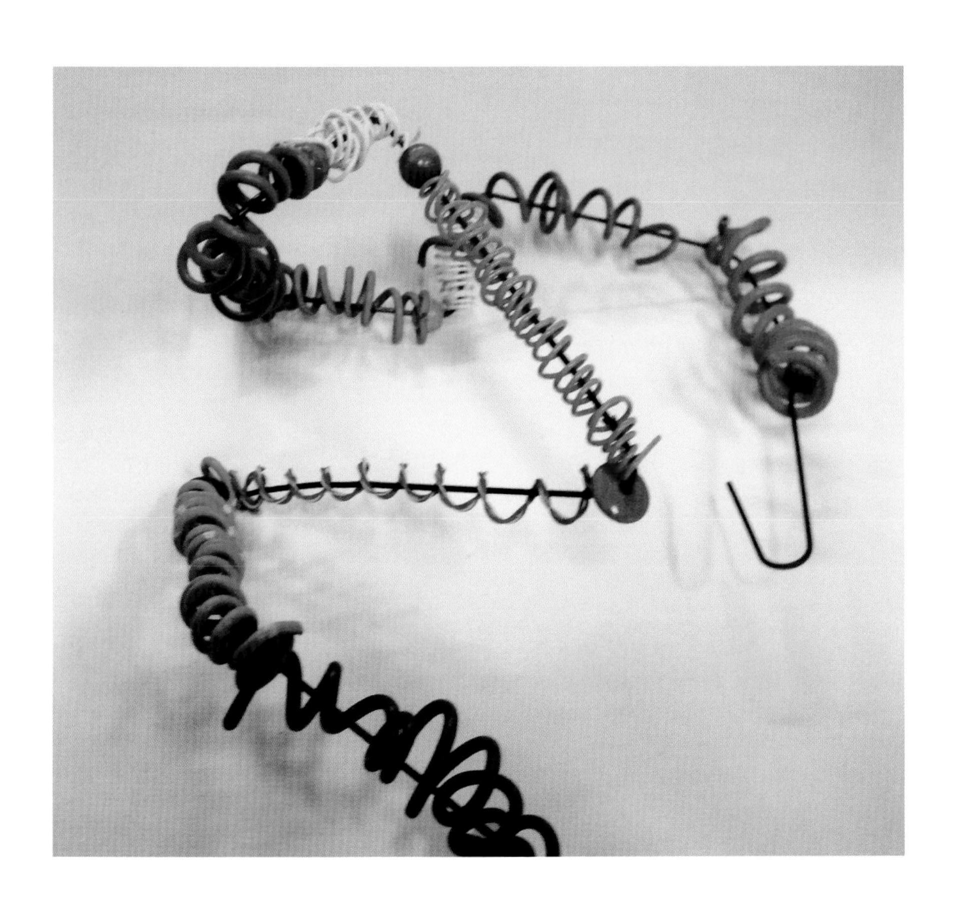

DNA

Telephone wires tangling together.
Springs bouncing out of place.
Spaghetti from a different galaxy.
Spaghetti is crawling down your settee.
Spaghetti is like telephone wires.
Eat it in the car and your mum will go
haywire.

Joe Evans Age 9

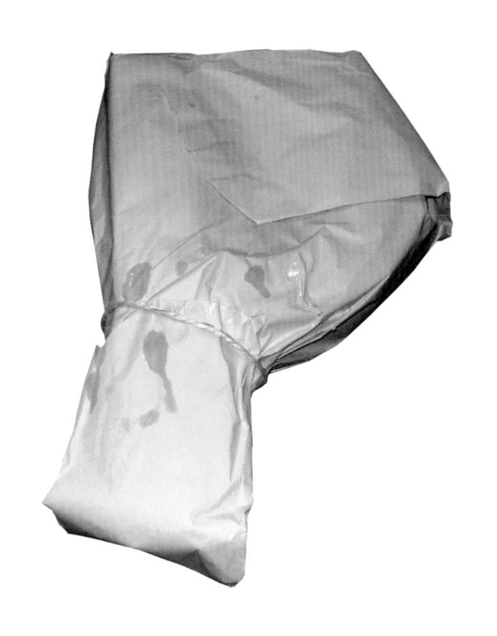

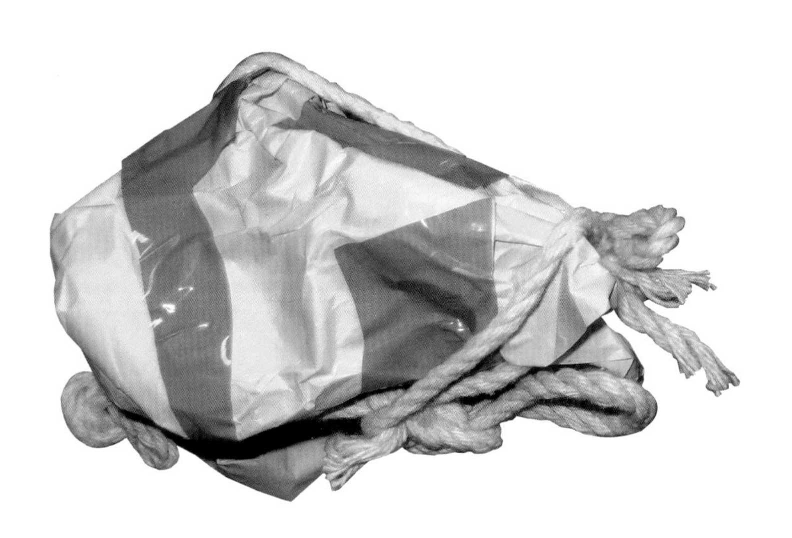

Pattern recognition

Richard Morris
John Innes Centre

I am a project leader in Computational & Systems Biology at the John Innes Centre. My main interests lie in the area of pattern recognition and information processing in biology.

pattern recognition

Dry Drayton Primary School

Teacher **Margaret Prosser**
Age range of children **7–11**

Scientist **Richard Morris**
Artist **Chris Hann**
Writer **Tom Corbett**

Once I got my head round the underlying idea of what a fractal is, then the objectives became much clearer.

Chris Hann Artist

During our SAW project we exposed children from ages 7–11 to nonlinear dynamics, chaos and fractals. These are very advanced and challenging concepts, well beyond most undergraduate courses in maths or physics. To our great astonishment, the children's openness towards new ideas and eagerness to play with new exciting things allowed them to grasp many of the concepts without being held back by the prejudice of it all being too difficult for them. The children were enchanted by this strange new world of fractal universes and recursive monsters that was presented to them. It was great to see how well the children responded. I think we all found SAW a hugely rewarding experience.

Richard Morris Scientist

1 A computer graphics image entitled 'Found in Space'. The image was derived from a Newtonian Equation, a group of complex numbers plotted using their real and imaginary parts as coordinates. Each point is assigned a colour depending upon its behaviour under a series of simple but repeated mathematical operations or mappings. Such 'chaotic' operations may be used to model real-world phenomena such as stock market prices, population dynamics and fluid interactions.
Image: Gregory Sams/Science Photo Library.

2 Mandelbrot fractal. Computer artwork of a part of the Mandelbrot Set, a pattern generated using a simple repeating mathematical process (named after the mathematician Benoit B. Mandelbrot). The process of repetition (called iteration) is applied to a set of complex numbers. The patterns formed are infinitely complicated, appearing qualitatively the same on whatever scale they are viewed.
Image: Pasieka/Science Photo Library.

3 Mandelbrot fractal. Computer-generated image derived from a Mandelbrot Set.
Image: Friedrich Saurer/ Science Photo Library

4 Dragon tail fractal, computer artwork.
Image: Laguna Design/Science Photo Library.

5 Julia fractal. Computer-generated fractal derived from the Julia Set. The Julia Set is a class of shapes plotted from complex number coordinates. It was invented and studied during World War I by the French mathematicians, Gaston Julia and Pierre Fatou.
Image: Victor Habbick Visions/Science Photo Library.

6 Romanesco broccoli (*Brassica* sp.) florets. The spiral shapes of the florets describe a Fibonacci mathematical series, one in which each number is the sum of two previous numbers. For example: 0, 1, 1, 2, 3, 5, 8, 13, 21, and so on. This series was discovered by Italian mathematician Leonardo Fibonacci (1170–1240) and many natural patterns can be described using it. The florets are edible, and are a good source of vitamins A and C, and of the essential minerals iron and potassium.
Image: Steve Allen/Science Photo Library.

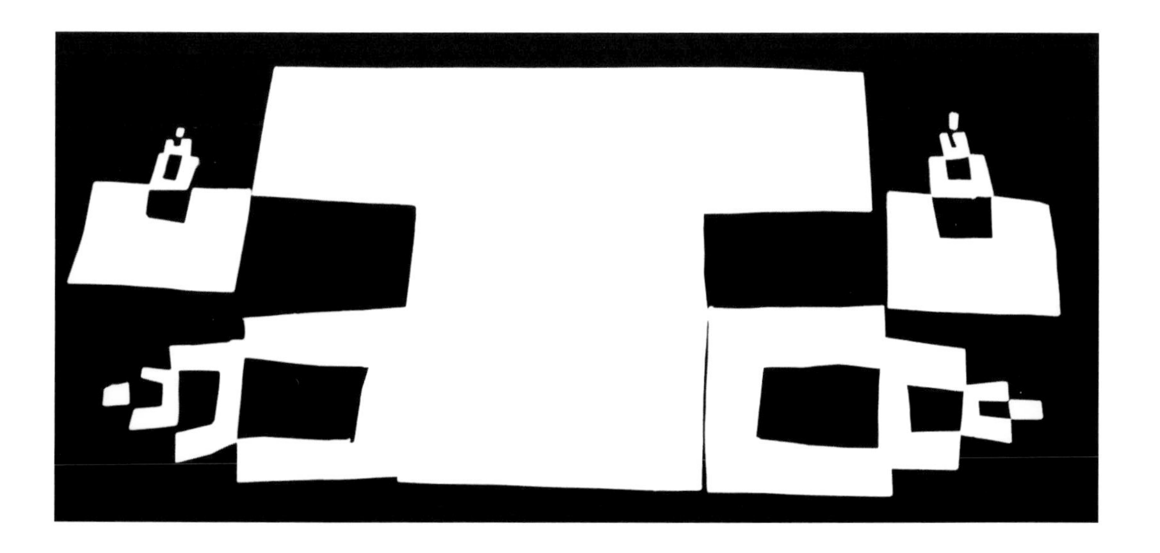

Jewellery fractal

I am the jewellery fractal
mistress and will now make
the sky turn into jewels.
I will make the ocean turn
into tiny sky blue crystals.
I will make jewellery for
animals.
I will make jewellery for the
moon and all the planets.
I will throw crystals into
the sky.
I will put pink crystals in
the clouds.

Nadine Kersey Age 9

Pet zoo of fractals

I went to a zoo
to get a pet fractal dragon
but they're
far too small.
I found a de-shrinker.
It became gigantic.
I had to push it with all my might.
It made a funny noise...
Gwagasalla.
It got out
now it smashed all of the other cages
they took over the world,
the master with a 700-eyed,
100-legged elephant.

Brian Morris Age 8

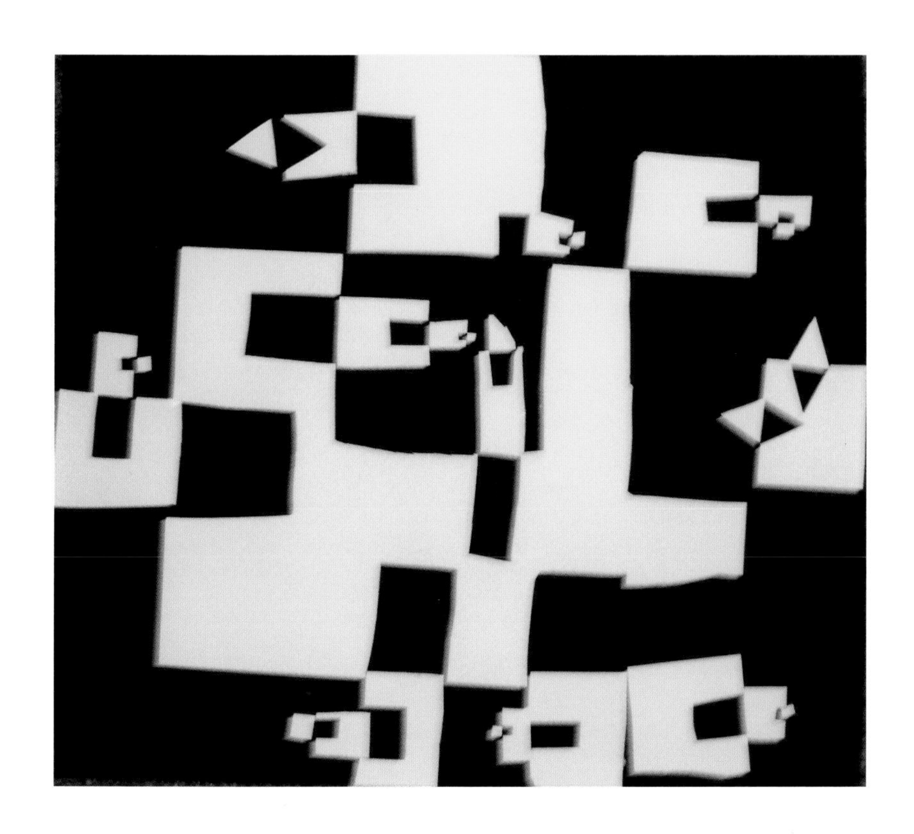

Fractal master of giant evil caterpillars

I am the master fractal
giant evil caterpillar
I shall get this caterpillar
and make it grow
bigger and bigger
I shall send it into space
and scare the earth
and let out a thunderous fractal roar.

Patrick Silvester Age 7

Space fairground fractal

Infinity slides
taking you everywhere,
the slides twisting and turning
making you sick
climbing up,
then swooping down
out of control,
floating like a feather
eating everything,
rotting your teeth
with every bite of fractal candyfloss,
animals leaping wildly
then falling back
down to Earth from space,
the space fairground fractalised
until next time.

Rebecca Dannert Age 10

Meristems

Robert Sablowski
John Innes Centre

Plants produce new organs such as leaves and floral organs throughout their lifetime. The cells required to build these organs are recruited from pools of actively dividing cells called the meristems. This continuous supply of new cells is sustained by small groups of self-renewing cells that reside at the core of the meristems and are functionally similar to stem cells in animals. My group has been interested in how regulatory genes control the behaviour of cells to maintain the meristem, or develop floral organs.

Avenue Junior School

Teacher **Tiffany Lacey-Edwards**
Age range of children **8-9**

Scientist **Robert Sablowski**
Artist **Chris Hann**
Writer **Mike O'Driscoll**

The children gave surprisingly well-informed and thoughtful answers to complex questions related to the similarities and differences between art and science.

Robert Sablowski Scientist

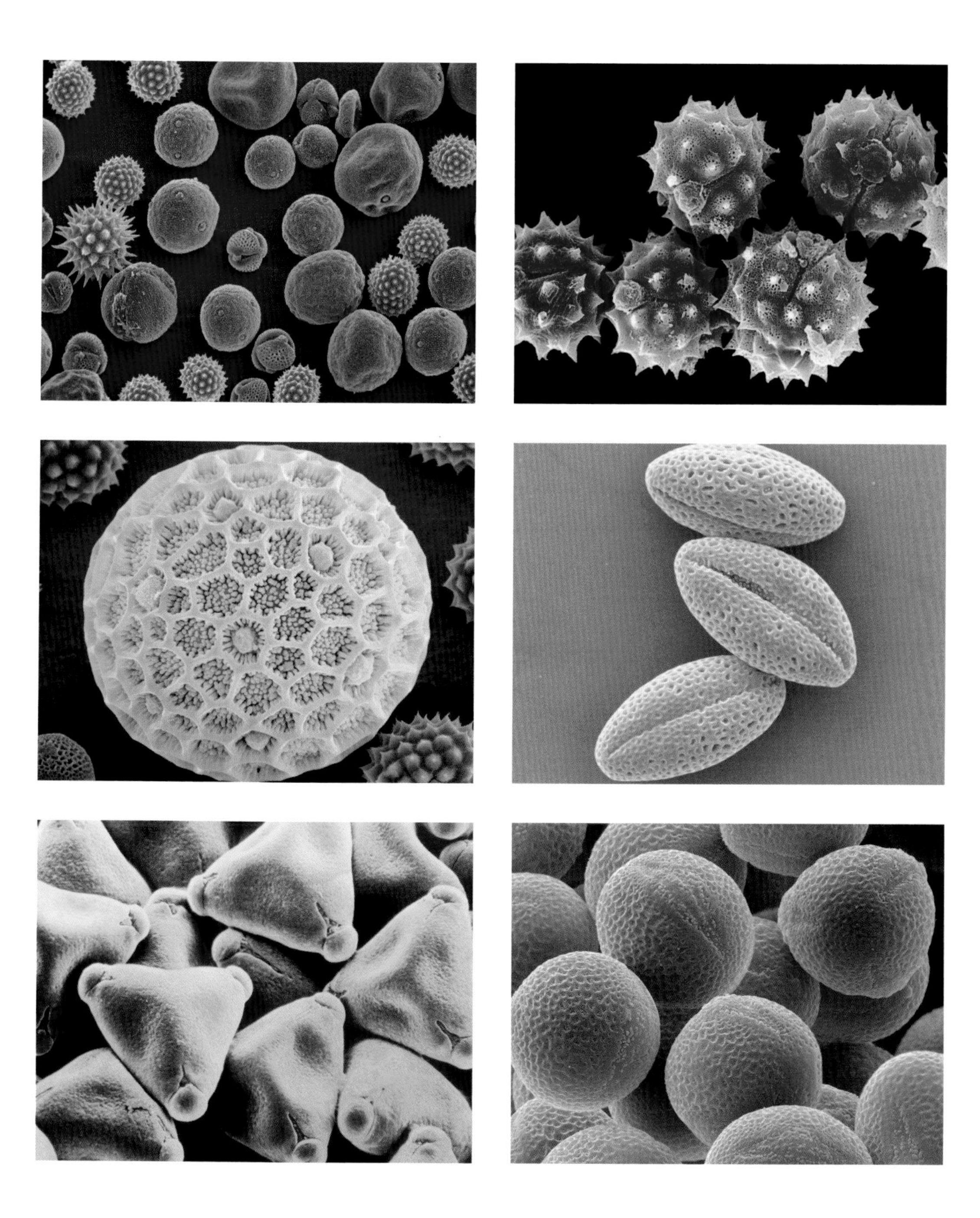

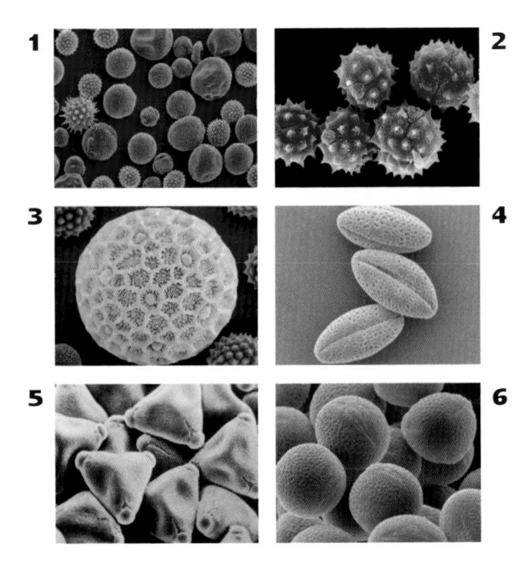

1 Coloured scanning electron micrograph (SEM) of an assortment of pollen grains. Pollen grain size, shape and surface texture differ from one plant species to another, as seen here. The outer wall (exine) of the pollen in many plant species is highly sculpted which may assist in wind, water or insect dispersal.

Image: David Scharf/Science Photo Library.

2 SEM of pollen grains from the daisy flower (family *Asteraceae*). The grains have a spiked outer wall (exine), which may assist in their dispersal by improving their adherence to pollinating insects.

Image: Philippe Psaila/Science Photo Library.

3 SEM of a pollen grain of the knotweed, *Polygonum* sp. The pollen grain is spherical. It has a highly sculpted outer wall (exine) of tiny columns (bacula), some fused at their tips to form ridges or walls (muri) arranged in a network. The ridges enclose irregular-shaped areas studded with granular wart-like processes.

Image: David Scharf/Science Photo Library.

4 SEM of pollen grains from an oilseed rape flower (*Brassica napus*). The outer wall (exine) of each grain is highly sculpted to improve its adherence to pollinating insects. Each grain has three furrows through which the pollen tube emerges at the time of germination.

Image: Biomedical Imaging Unit, Southampton General Hospital/Science Photo Library.

5 SEM of pollen grains of the wax plant, *Hoya carnosa*. These grains are triangular and smooth-walled, indicating wind dispersal.

Image: Science Photo Library.

6 SEM of pollen grains of red clover, *Trifolium pratense*. The outer wall (exine) of each grain has a netted ornamentation, and there are grooves called germinal furrows. These pollen grains are wind dispersed. When a pollen grain, containing the male gametes, lands on the stigma of a flower, it germinates. A pollen tube grows out from the furrow, down through the stigma, to the ovary. The male nuclei pass down this tube, fertilize the ovules and seeds are formed.

Image: Andrew Syred/Science Photo Library.

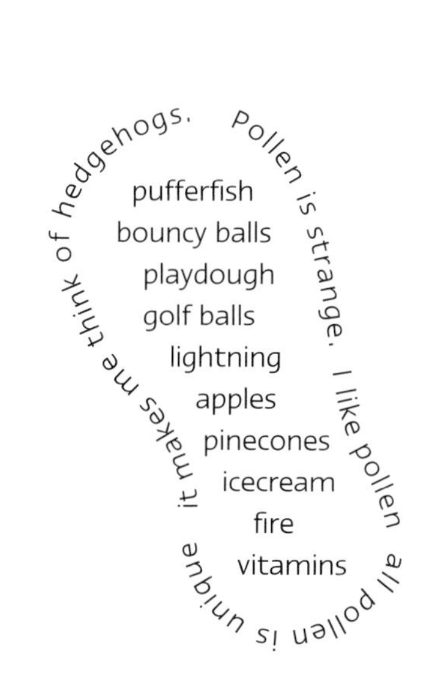

Pollen is strange. I like pollen all pollen is unique it makes me think of hedgehogs.

pufferfish
bouncy balls
playdough
golf balls
lightning
apples
pinecones
icecream
fire
vitamins

Madeleine Caynes Age 8

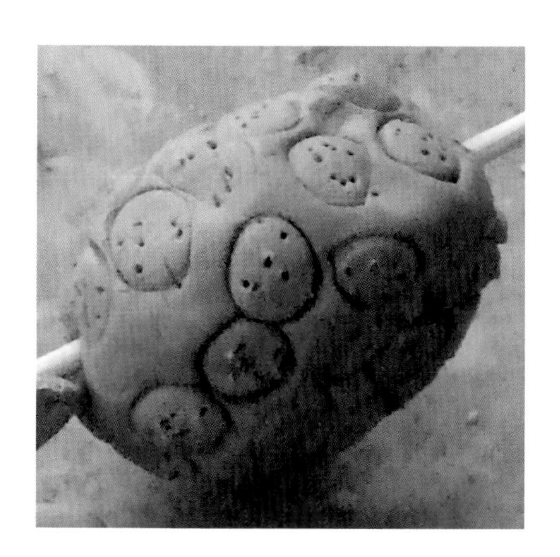

Buzzy bee

Buzzy buzzy bee
Buzzy bee you buzz round me
Buzzy buzzy bee

Leila Hooton Age 9

Pollen

Pollen can be red, blue and green,
the most amazing thing you've ever seen,
pollen looks like triangles,
or it can look like circles.

Doug Beckett Age 9

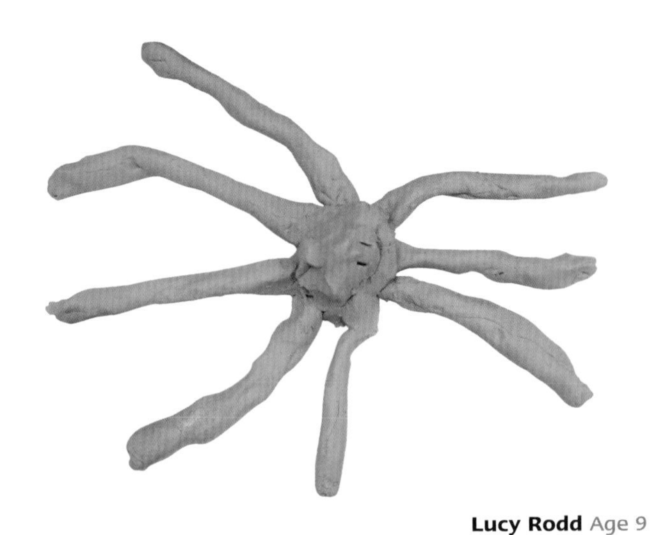

Lucy Rodd Age 9

Pollen

Lumpy bumpy
brainy stripy
squishy slimy
floaty scared
golf balls
sandy shelly
slippery white
and grey dotty.

Dominic Temple-Wilson Age 9

What pollen looks like

Ice cream scoops
spiky balls
rotten apples
Ccoloured bubble gum
red Doritos
firing comet
big brown shoes
orange, red and blue

George Sanders Age 8

Haiku

pollen is unique
no pollen is ever the same
they go their own way.

Madeleine Caynes Age 8

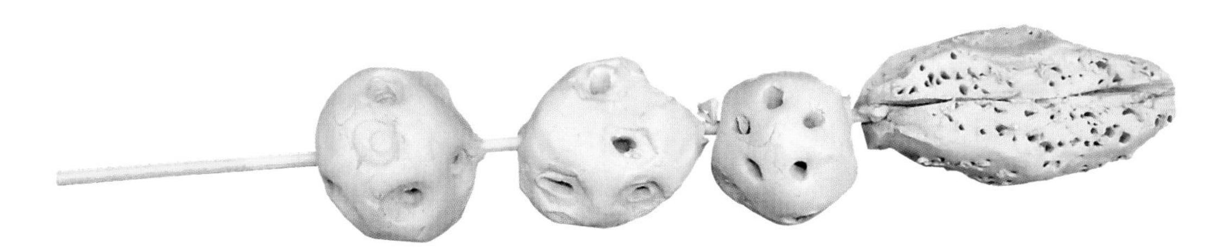

Luke Coyte-Mackenzie Age 9

Air raiders

Smells like smoky barbecue melted chocolate.
Looks like ball brain plant and pom poms.
Tastes like strawberry chewing gum.
Sounds like a trumpet in the distance.
Feels like a soft round sponge.

Heather Blaseby Age 9

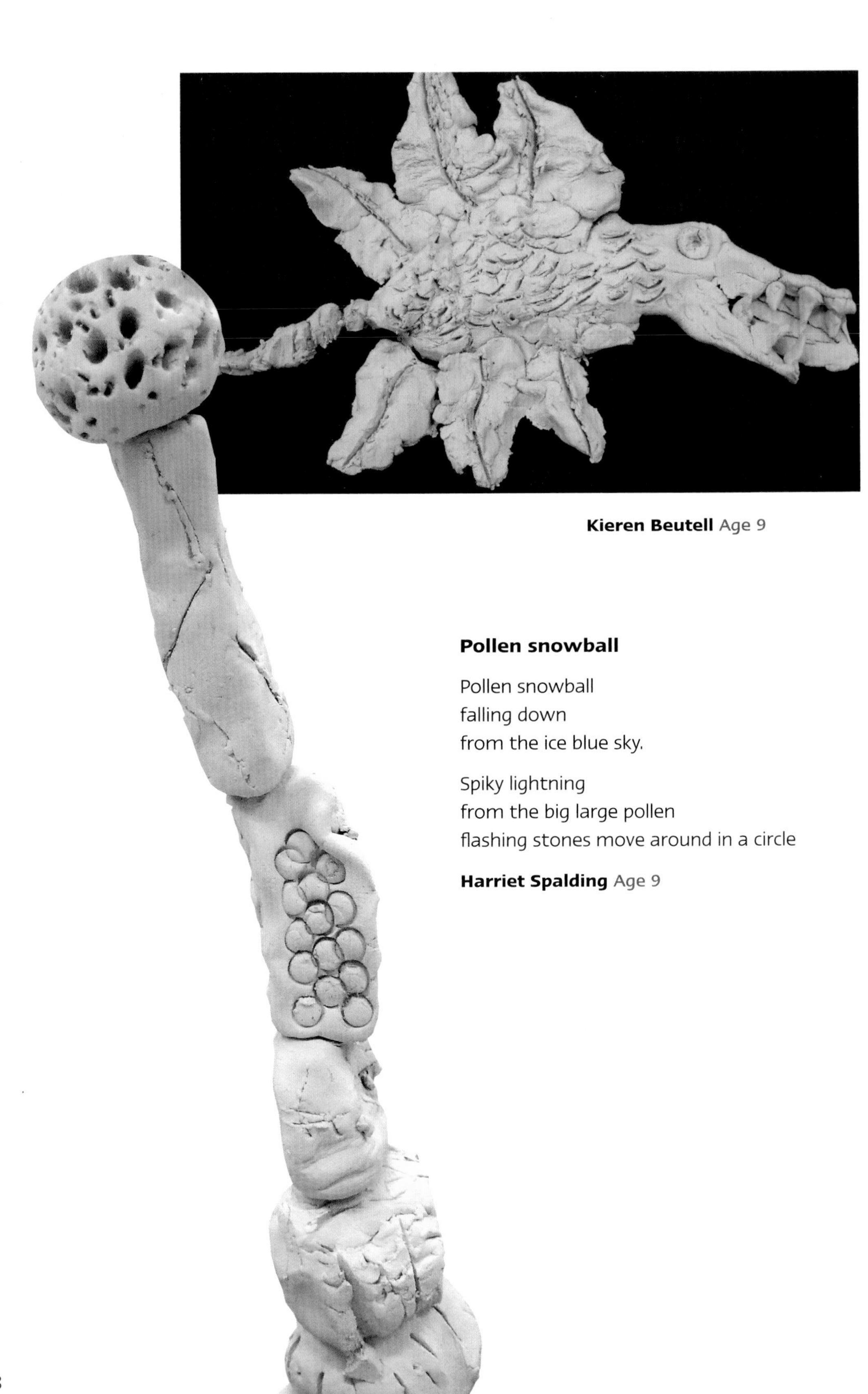

Kieren Beutell Age 9

Pollen snowball

Pollen snowball
falling down
from the ice blue sky.

Spiky lightning
from the big large pollen
flashing stones move around in a circle

Harriet Spalding Age 9

genetic modification

Genetic modification

John Innes Centre

Wendy Harwood

Wendy is a strategic research scientist leading a group working on genetically modified (GM) crops. Her group is working on ways to improve the methods for producing GM crops and looking at the safety of GM crops and the food derived from them.

Rachel Wells

Rachel is a molecular geneticist working in a group that studies oilseed rape. She is currently involved in projects researching plant architecture to improve seed yield and the production of biolubricants from rapeseed oil.

Hayley Jeffries

Hayley is a junior research assistant within a group working on the crop plant oilseed rape. Her work is on the architecture of this species, looking at how the plants grow and finding ways of increasing the yield produced.

Jo Bartlett

Jo is a final-year PhD student and her research is focused on the genetic modification of barley. She is looking at ways to control the activity of the genes introduced to the barley plant.

St Mary's Church of England Junior School, Long Stratton

Teacher **Jo Gray**
Age range of children **10–11**

Scientists **Wendy Harwood, Rachel Wells, Jo Bartlett and Hayley Jeffries**
Artist **Sarah Jarrett**
Writer **Mike O'Driscoll**

The project helps the children to see they can use science and link it to art and writing. They can make it creative and are allowed to let their imaginations run riot.

Jo Gray Class teacher and deputy head

The SAW day we spent at St Mary's Junior School, Long Stratton, was an extremely rewarding experience. The children loved investigating the different types of seeds and learning about their dispersal methods. The energy and enthusiasm they had for all of the activities was brilliant to watch and overall the day was a great success.

Wendy Harwood and Hayley Jeffries Scientists

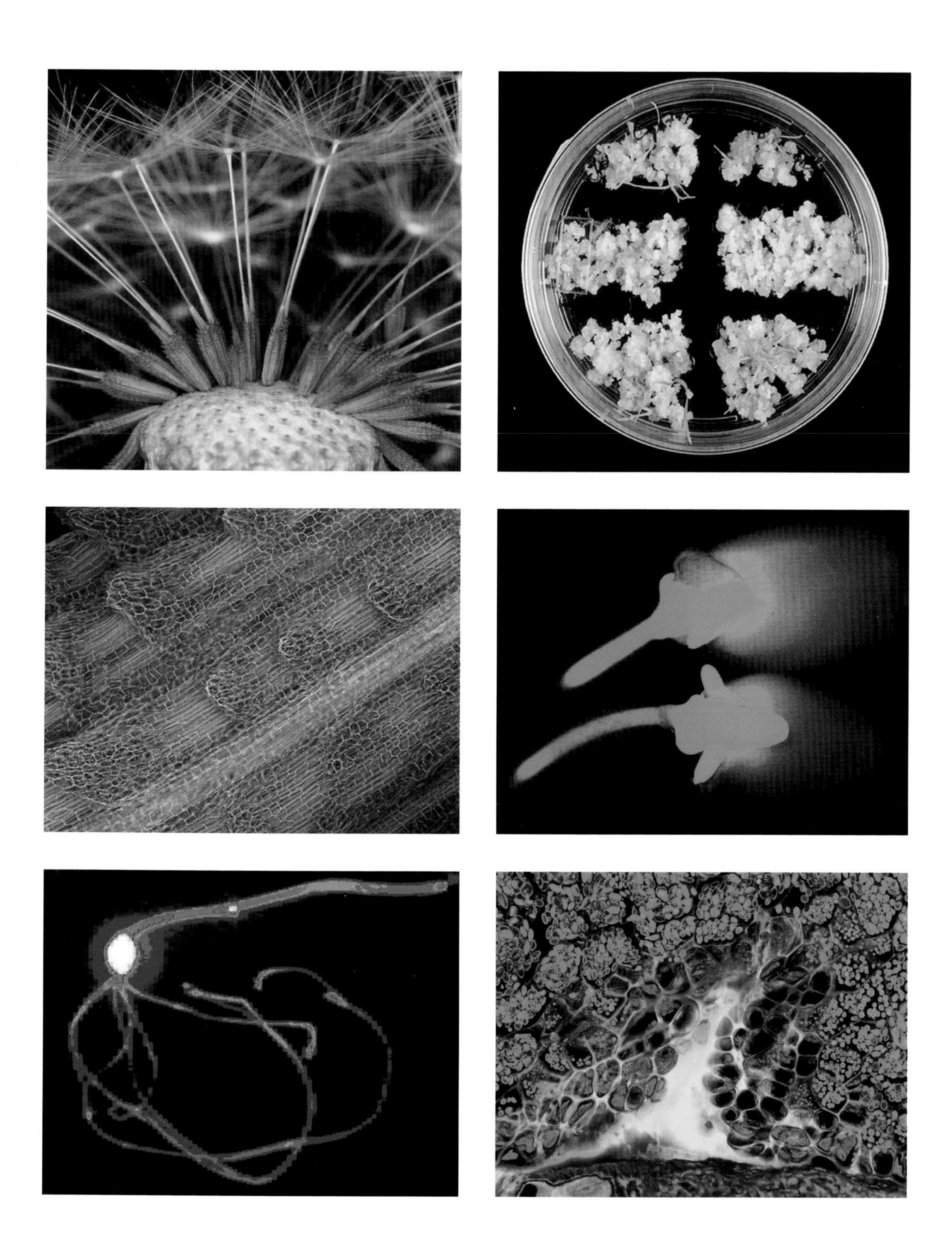

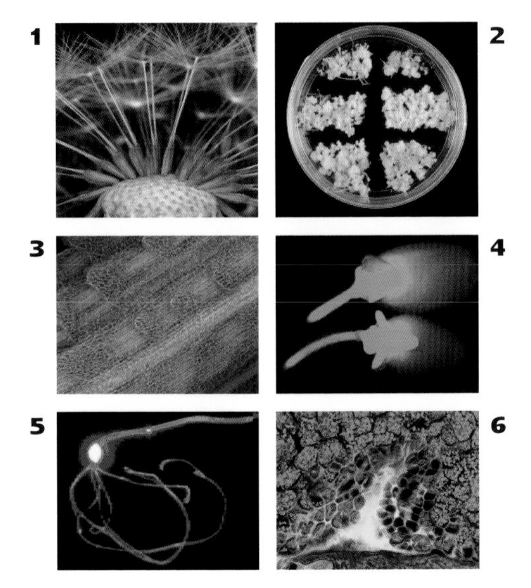

1 Dandelion seeds. The seeds of the dandelion (*Taraxacum officinale*) are so lightly held in place that the slightest of winds will set the seeds adrift in the air.
Image: Ted Kinsman/Science Photo Library.

2 Barley cultures showing the first signs of tiny plants developing.
Image: Wendy Harwood.

3 A close-up of a dandelion seed showing the patterns on the surface.
Image: National High Magnetic Field Laboratory, Florida State University.

4 Glowing wheat seeds that contain a green fluorescent protein.
Image: Huw D. Jones & Julia Goodwin, Rothamsted Research.

5 A glowing barley seedling showing the roots and shoot emerging from the glowing grain.
Image: Wendy Harwood.

6 A close-up of the inside of a wheat grain.
Image: National High Magnetic Field Laboratory, Florida State University.

Derek the alien

He crawls out of his space-pod
and stretches his many arms out wide.
His body is a sapphire blue
with mixtures of greens and red in it.
He has landed on Planet Earth
in a dense forest with bugs and beetles,
he slithered and wriggled over trees and plants
to a nearby town called Ipswich.

Adam Saunders Age 11

Me the seed!!

Today I was born,
with lots of others,
guess what I am,
a dandelion seed.
Well that's what my mother said,
she says I will leave one day,
what does she mean?
She says a journey.

I am coming loose,
from my mother,
oh no she's right,
I will go on a journey.

A day later I land,
I am underground,
I am getting bigger,
every day I am twice the size,
than I was the day before.

About a day later,
I see the glorious sun,
I still keep getting bigger,
it's warm now.
What am I?
A FLOWER!!

Zoe Smith Age 11

My tree

Shiny little tiny seeds
that fly in the sky
floating on the turquoise sea as you walk by.
As it grows into a sapling it looks like a
small mouse that is
covered in a protector that they call a
little house.
After a wait it grows
into a young tree
as green as a
light blue sea.
Growing and growing
into a chestnut tree
already nearly as tall
as me!
Another year goes
and the tree it still grows.

Amber Wilson Age 10

The green waves rushing by

The green waves are rushing by
oh what shall we do?
Should we try to count them
or maybe even ride on them?
Should we search for fish,
should we swim on them
or should we just sit down
and watch the green waves rush by.

Brendan Edwards Age 10

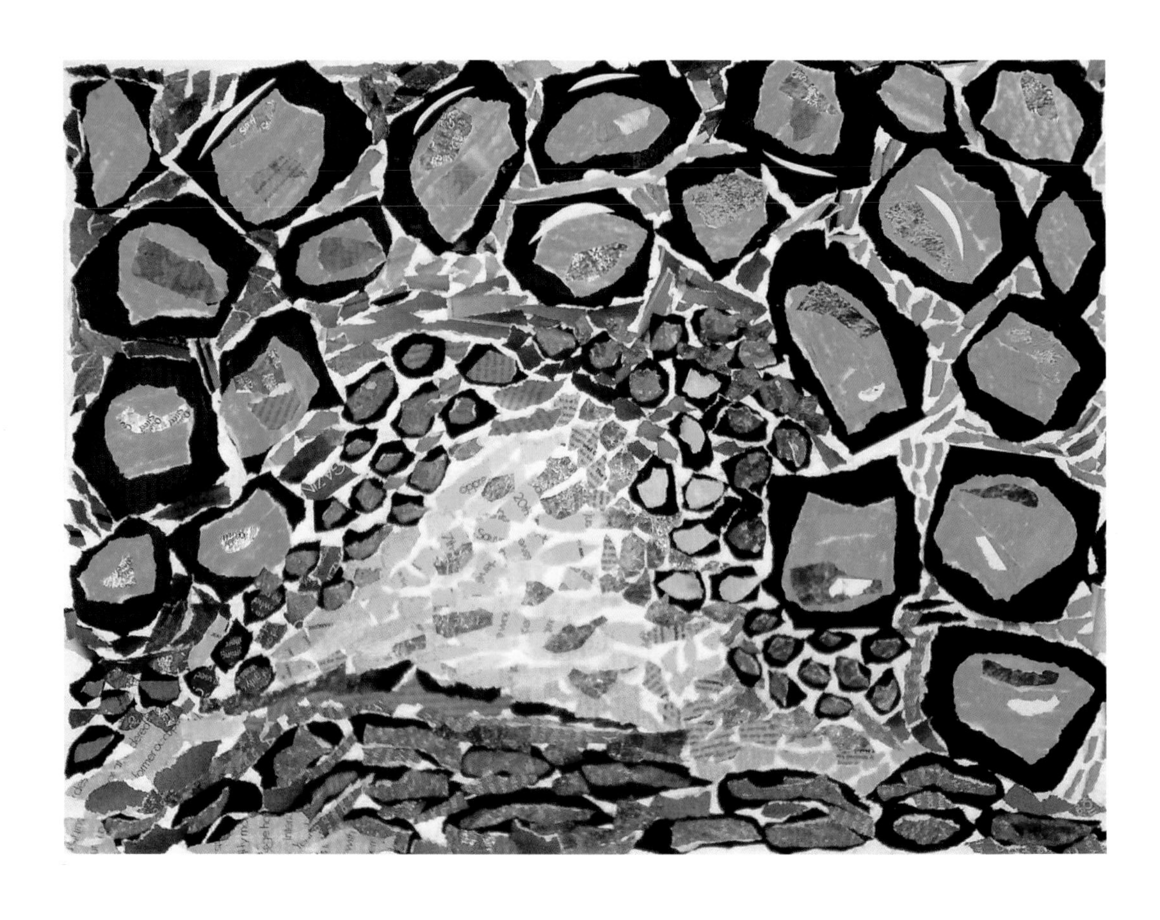

Pathogens

Jenni Rant
John Innes Centre

Andrew Staphnill
John Innes Centre

Plants are sessile organisms and need to have defence mechanisms that protect them from potential sources of harm in their environment. Pathogens such as bacteria, fungi and viruses can infect plants and cause disease. In food crops this can have a large detrimental effect on the harvest and, in wild plants, it can impact on the habitat of other organisms. Plants vary enormously in their ability to resist pathogens and many scientists at the John Innes Centre study the complex nature of plant disease resistance.

Jenni Rant and Andrew Staphnill are PhD students at the John Innes Centre from the department of Disease and Stress Biology. Jenni is using *Arabidopsis thaliana* as a model plant to investigate fitness costs in crops that may be associated with increased levels of resistance to pathogens. Andrew is studying the varying levels of disease resistance within different varieties of *Arabidopsis thaliana* and looking for genes that may be responsible.

The SAW project aimed to introduce the concept that plants get 'sick', just as we do, but are unable to move. We looked at symptoms under microscopes and explored how the crops we grow have been selectively bred for their resistance to particular diseases.

pathogens

Great Ellingham Primary School

Teacher **Ben Cole**
Age range of children **8–10**

Scientists **Jenni Rant and Andrew Staphnill**
Artist **Chris Hann**
Writer **Tom Corbett**

Diseases are like art because they are so beautiful.

Lauren McArdle Age 9

I learned that if you have an ice cube, ink and a pipette you can make a cool picture.

Daniel Wood Age 9

I learned that Japanese write down, not across.

Daisy Rant Age 9

I think other scientists should do this type of project as it's a great way to get our research out there to a wide audience and it sparks a lot of interest and confidence in children to do more science.

Jenni Rant Scientist

In many ways it is more difficult to simplify a complex issue than to explain every aspect of the problem. Therefore it was an invaluable experience to be offered a young audience to communicate science with.

Andrew Staphnill Scientist

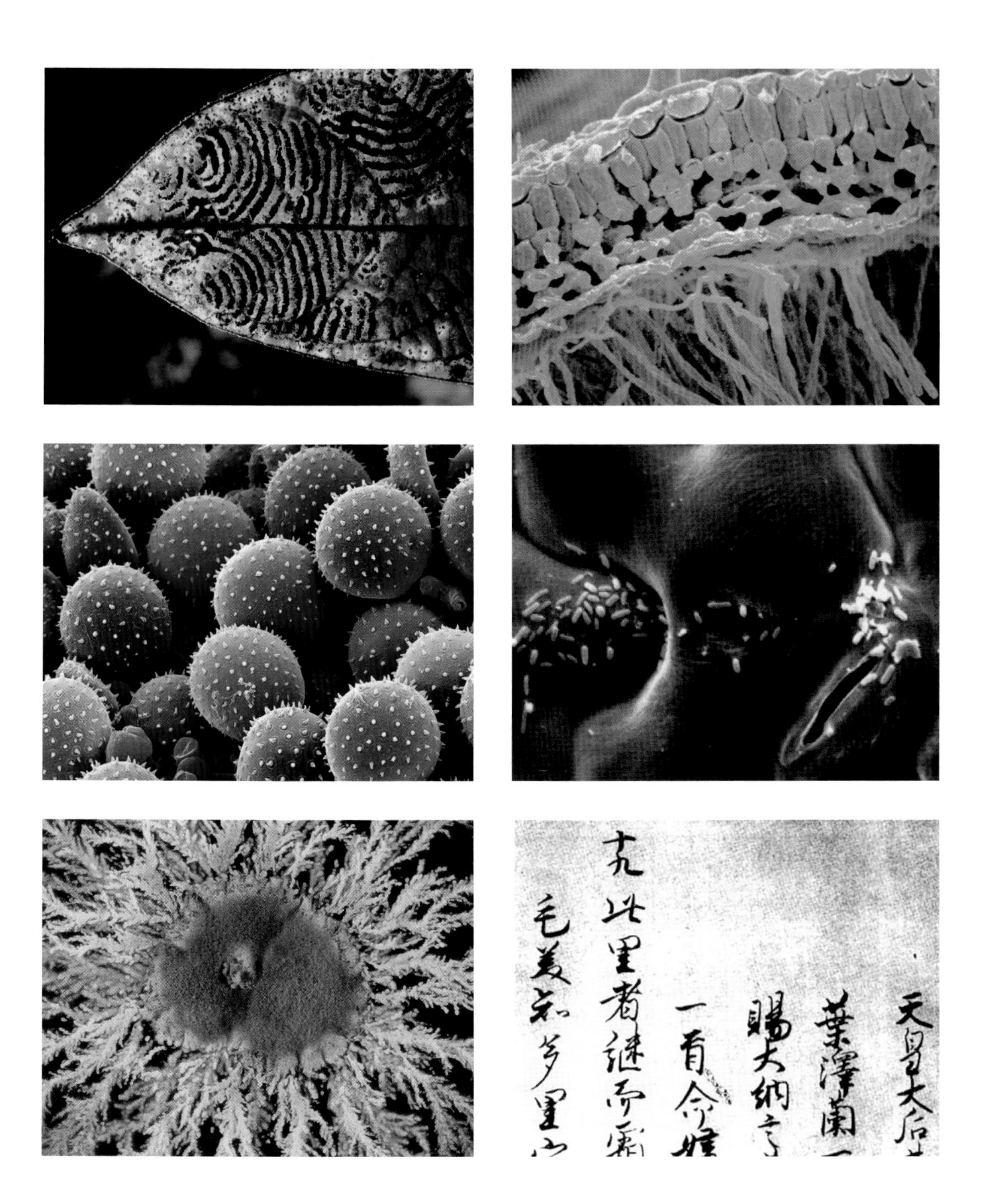

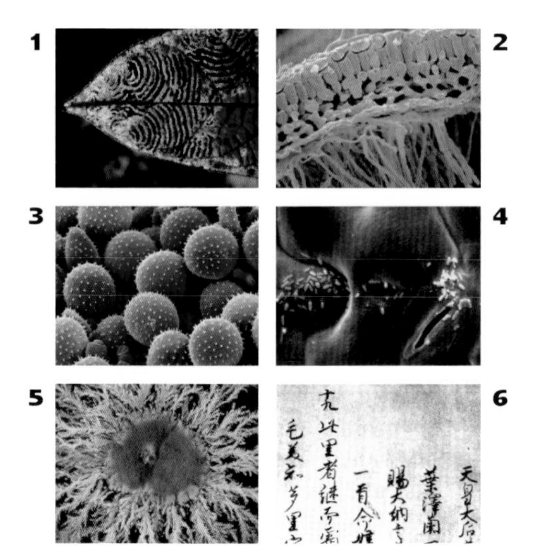

1 Unidentified fungus on a rainforest leaf -maybe an early inspiration for tribal art? The leaf comes from a tree in the montane rain forest at Mindo in Ecuador.
Image: Dr Morley Read/Science Photo Library.

2 Mildew on leaf. False-colour scanning electron micrograph (SEM) of a fractured transverse section through the leaf of a Michaelmas daisy, *Aster* sp. infected with a mildew fungus. Cells of the daisy leaf are at the top; long hair-like hyphae of the fungus are seen on the underside of the leaf. Mildew is a common plant disease caused by a number of fungal species; it refers to the appearance of the infected plant, the leaves of which look as if they have been dusted with a powdery or downy growth.
Image: Andrew Syred/Science Photo Library.

3 Close-up of rust fungal spores (they look like sea anemones). SEM of spores from a rust fungus that infects rose plants. Rust fungi (order *Uredinales*) are parasites that attack plants. They are very specific to their host plant, and reproduce by the dispersal of spores that form red rust-like areas on the leaves and stems of diseased plants. They are of economic importance as they can reduce crop yields.
Image: Steve Gschmeissner/Science Photo Library.

4 The bacteria, *Pseudomonas*, about to invade the surface of a leaf by entering a stoma.
Image: Joanne Morello, Cornell University.

5 The eyespot fungus *Pseudocercosporella herpatrichoides* overwinters on infected stubble in fields and then attacks the leaf sheath of the following year's crop and causes lesions on the stems.
Image: Paul Nicholson.

6 A Japanese poem written in AD 752 that is the first written record of a plant virus (although unknowingly). This poem is taken from the Rui-shu-ko-shu edition of the *Man'yoshu* edited by Atsukata Furiwara (AD 1071–1120).
Image: Adapted by permission from Macmillan Publishers Ltd: *Nature* 422: 831, copyright 2003.

Top
of a green
African shield with curly,
swirly patterns. A lovely butterfly
wing made like a peacock's tail feather. The maps
roads are like the veins in your fingers. A mountain with tracks
and trees. And the trees with green leaves are like the top of an African shield.

Leah Garnham Age 10

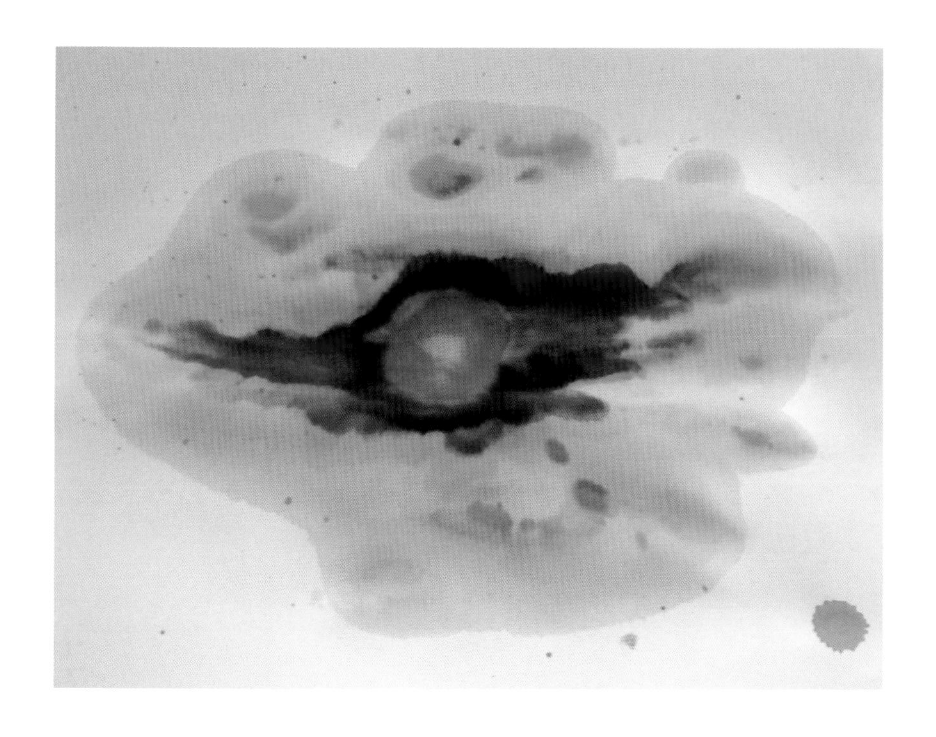

I am

I am
young
my leaves
are bright
my flowers
are strong.

Ella-May Age 9

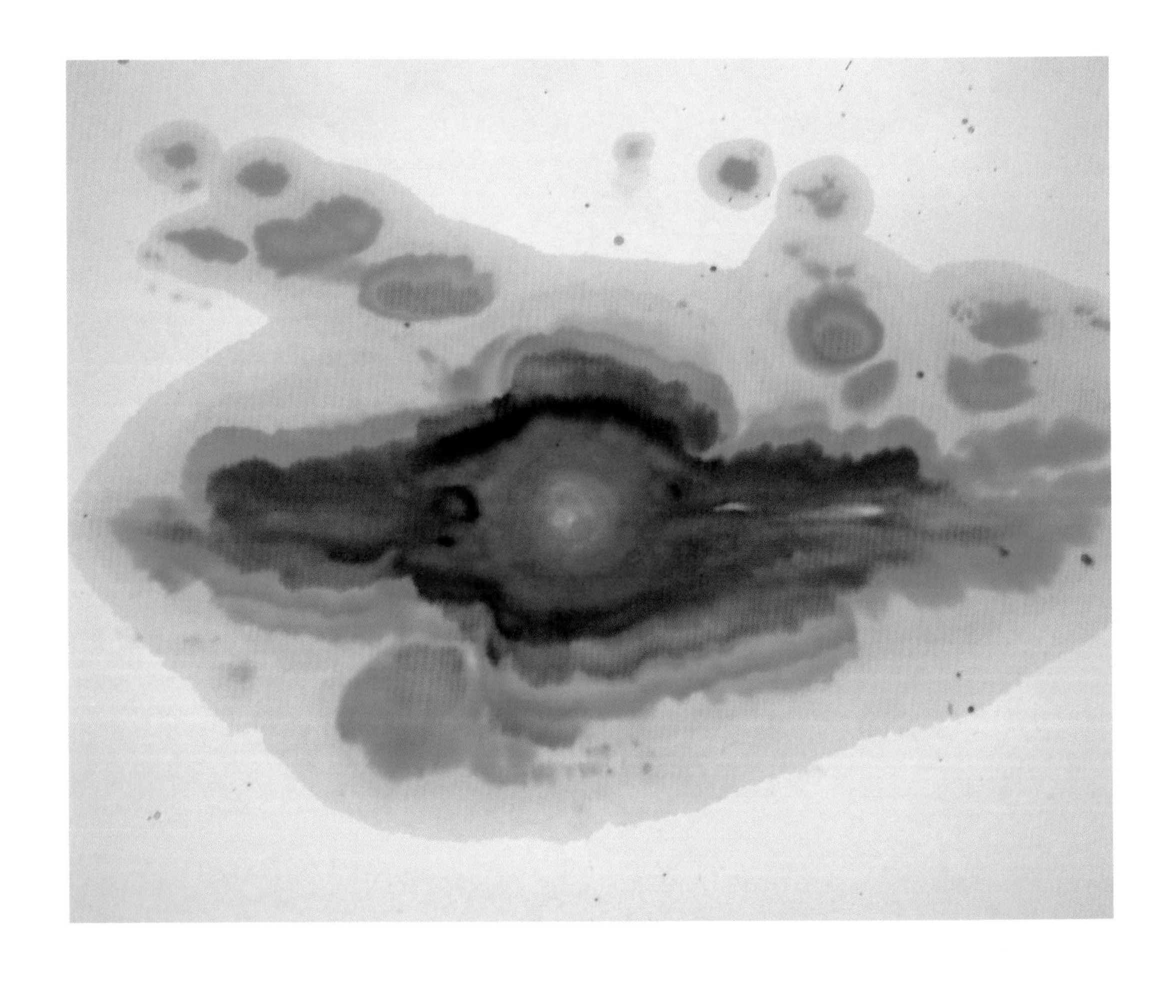

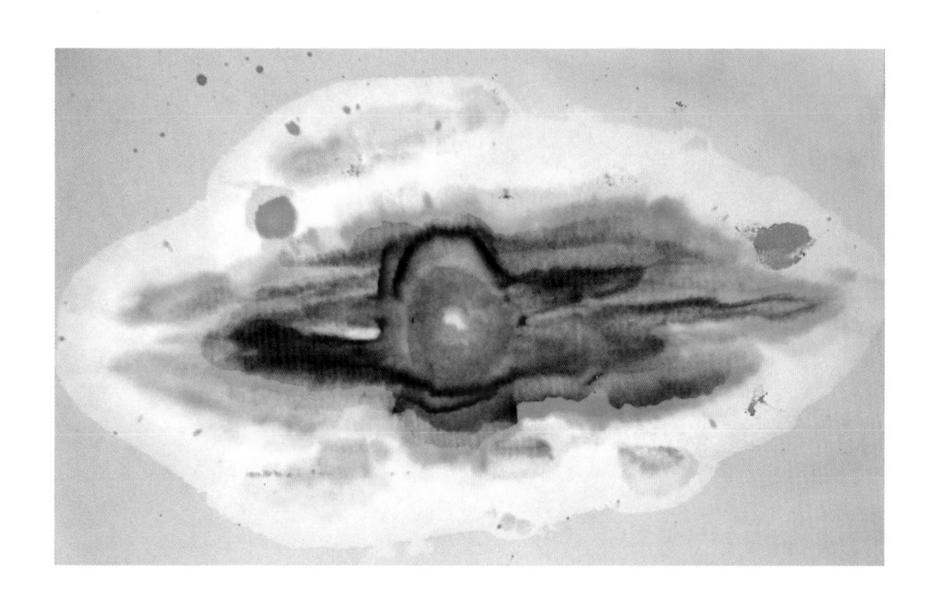

Eupatorium

I am Eupatorium.
I am beautiful and green and yellow
but beneath
my beautiful
green leaves
lays a disease
so do not be fooled
by exteriors
as if you touch me
you
will
catch
a
disease.

James Lavall Age 9

This is for you my love

This is for you my love,
remember this plant,
that I gave you.
with my own love,
and my own heart,
that I cherish.

This plant, you will love,
it will live for a short time,
but I will always be here for you,
even when the plant dies.

Eleanor Bridge Age 10

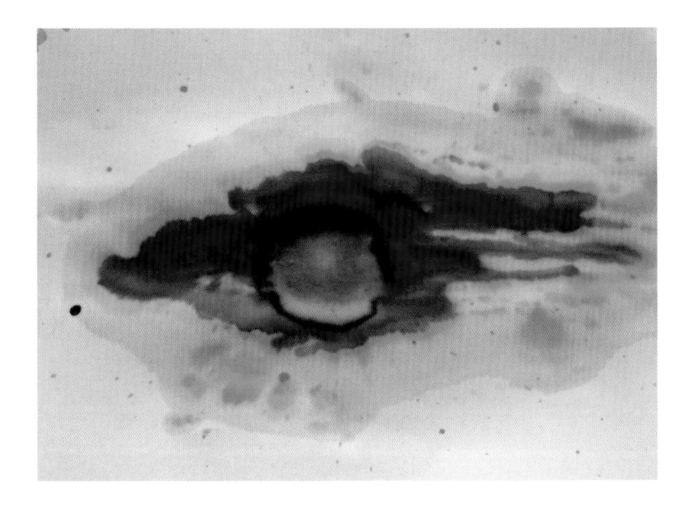

A strip in the sea

I am a winding road,
a strip in the sea
a heart of gold,
I'm love on a leaf.

Lauren McArdle Age 9

The disease

There once was a dragon that had a disease,
and when he stood up he fell on his knees.

There once was a girl who helped the dragon,
that had a disease.

She went to buy some medicine,
but when she went out she sneezed.

There once was a boy who helped the girl,
that gave a rather large sneeze.

He went to buy some medicine,
then he got the disease!

Holly Purdon Age 10

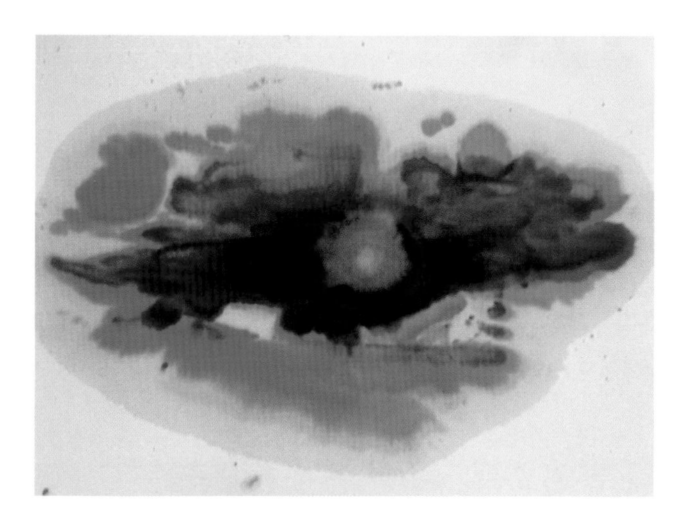

In AD 752 a Japanese man gave his love a flower,
it may have been a Eupatorium. I am English
so I give my love a rose.

You
are my
lover.
I miss
you so
much.
I want to
buy you
lots of
presents.
For when
I see
you
again.

I
love you
too. You are
the stars in
my eyes
I will come
back as
soon as
I can
to be
with
you.

Our
love is
very
strong.
It will
blossom
like a rose.
We will grow
together
for
eternity.
I will
never
leave
you again.

Courtney Age 10

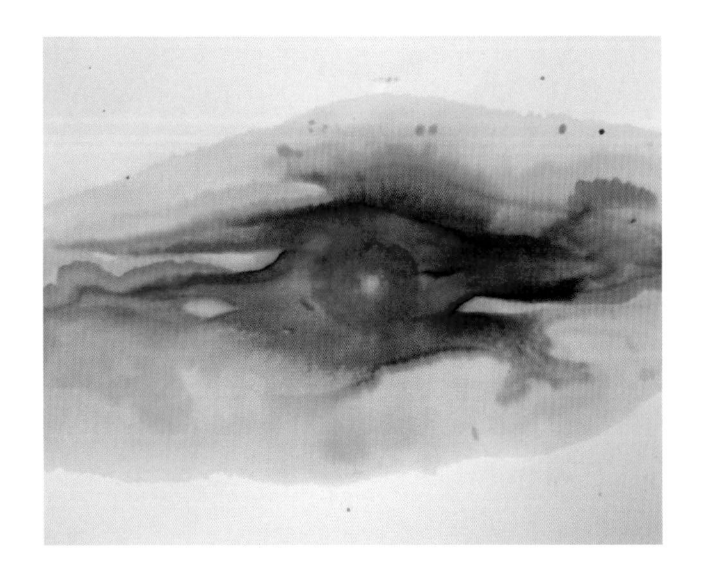

Immune regulation

Juan Arques Orobon
Institute of Food Research

Kamal Ivory
Institute of Food Research

Kamal works in the Gastrointestinal Biology and Health group at the Institute of Food Research where her research interests are fairly varied. She has recently completed a study on the immunomodulatory effects of probiotics in seasonal allergic rhinitis, and an ongoing collaborative study on the influence of selenium supplementation on viral immunity. However, her main focus is on examining immune regulation in food allergy, with particular emphasis on life-threatening peanut allergy.

Juan is a Microbiologist-Immunologist Research Scientist within the Mucosal Immunology group. He is currently focused on the interactions between bacteria and the gut-associated lymphoid tissue to understand their beneficial or pathogenic role, in order to identify the benefits of the probiotic bacteria and to prevent or treat pathogen infections.

Rockland St Mary Primary School

Teacher **Denise McGee**
Age range of children **9–11**

Scientists **Kamal Ivory and Juan Arques Orobon**
Artist **Sarah Jarrett**
Writer **Tom Corbett**

I was really surprised by the enthusiasm with which the children involved themselves in the SAW project – and the results were awe-inspiring. I was impressed at how clever the children were at grasping new concepts and how imaginative with their science-inspired poetry. The best part of all was seeing how much they enjoyed themselves, as did my scientific colleagues and I.

Kamal Ivory Scientist

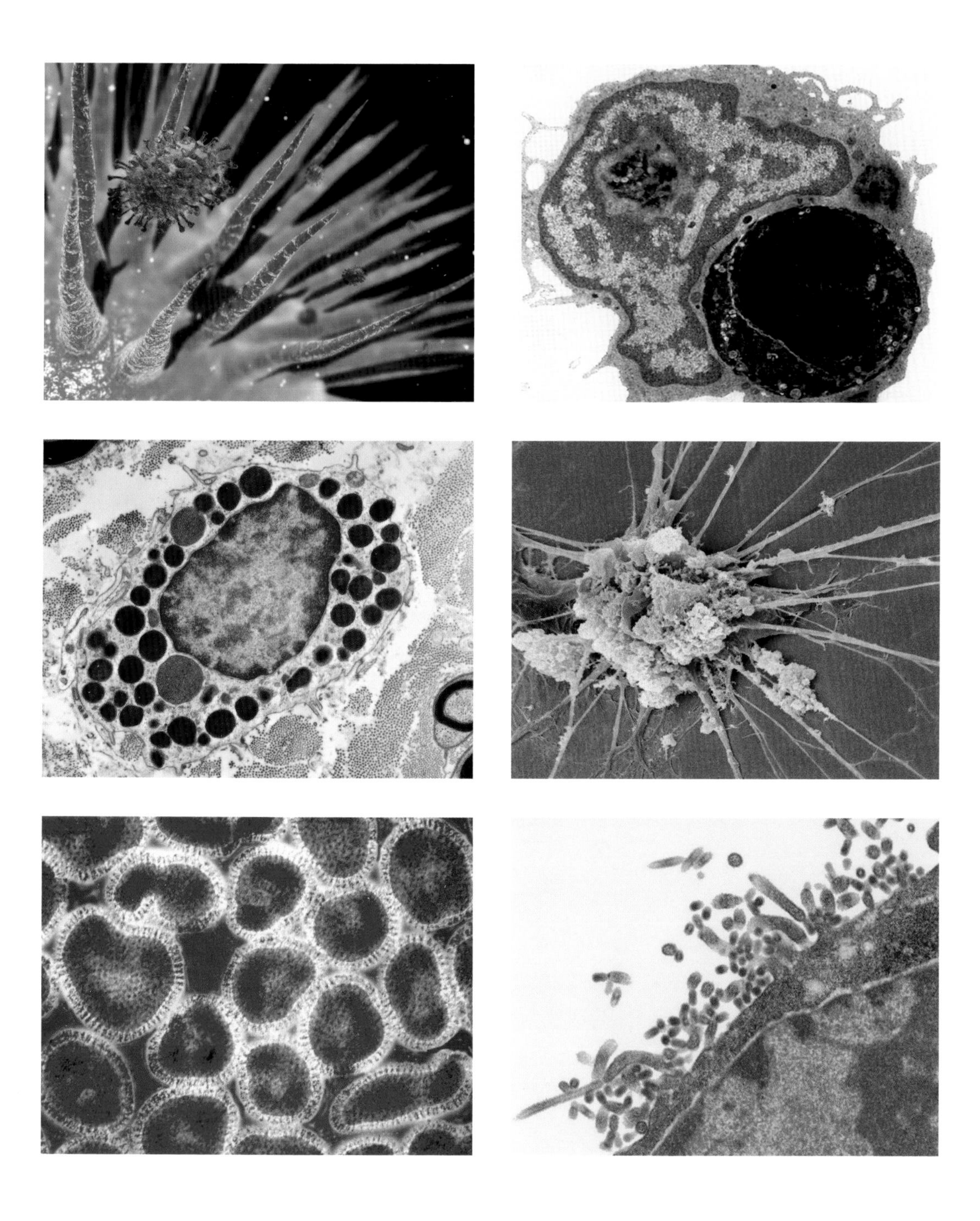

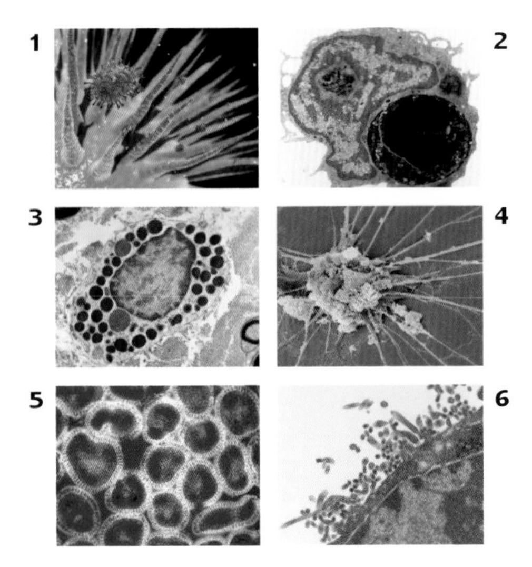

1 Conceptual image of influenza viruses (brown) in the airways of the lung. The virus particles are not at the same scale as the lung cilia (blue). Each virus consists of a core of RNA (ribonucleic acid) genetic material surrounded by a protein coat (brown). Embedded in the coat are surface proteins (spikes).

Image: Karsten Schneider/Science Photo Library.

2 A transmission electron micrograph (TEM) of a macrophage engulfing another cell. The process is called phagocytosis which derives from the Greek *phago* - to eat, *kytos* - cell, and *oasis* - a suffix indicating a process. It translates literally as 'the cellular process of eating' and is one way in which specialised cells (phagocytes) of the human body remove foreign bodies such as bacteria, infected cells and other unwanted material. Once inside the phagocyte, the ingested material is degraded by enzymes.

Image: Dr Jeremy Skepper/Wellcome Images.

3 Basophil. Coloured TEM of a section through a basophil white blood cell. The nucleus, which stores the cell's genetic information, is green. Basophils are cells of the body's immune system, involved in allergic and inflammatory reactions. They secrete the chemicals heparin, histamine and serotonin, which are stored in granules (brown) in the cell's cytoplasm. Basophils are the smallest and least common of the white blood cells.

Image: Steve Gschmeissner/Science Photo Library.

4 Coloured scanning electron micrograph (SEM) of a neuron (nerve cell). The cell body is the central structure with neurites (long and thin structures) radiating outwards from it.

Image: Steve Gschmeissner/Science Photo Library.

5 TEM of influenza viruses. The 'flu' virus belongs to the orthomyxovirus group of viruses. It contains a core of RNA (ribonucleic acid) genetic material inside a protein coat or capsid. Spikes form a fringe around the capsid and allow the virus to attach to its host cell. Influenza is an infection of the respiratory tract. It causes a fever, aching muscles, a sore throat and weakness. Mutant strains of influenza sometimes appear, and can cause fatal epidemics.

Image: Dr Gopal Murti/Science Photo Library.

6 Coloured TEM of influenza viruses (red) budding from a host cell. The host cell nucleus is yellow.

Image: Steve Gschmeissner/Science Photo Library.

The cell

Like holey cheese floating in the blackness of the universe,
a green pea the size of a flea falling through never-ending nothingness,
tense like a planet ready to explode and drop endlessly through space,
as green as frog spawn lying at the bottom of a river of pure black water,
isolated and defenceless as the inside of a lettuce,
the evergreen mould off a piece of bread shut in a cramped old cupboard.

Jake Brown Age 10

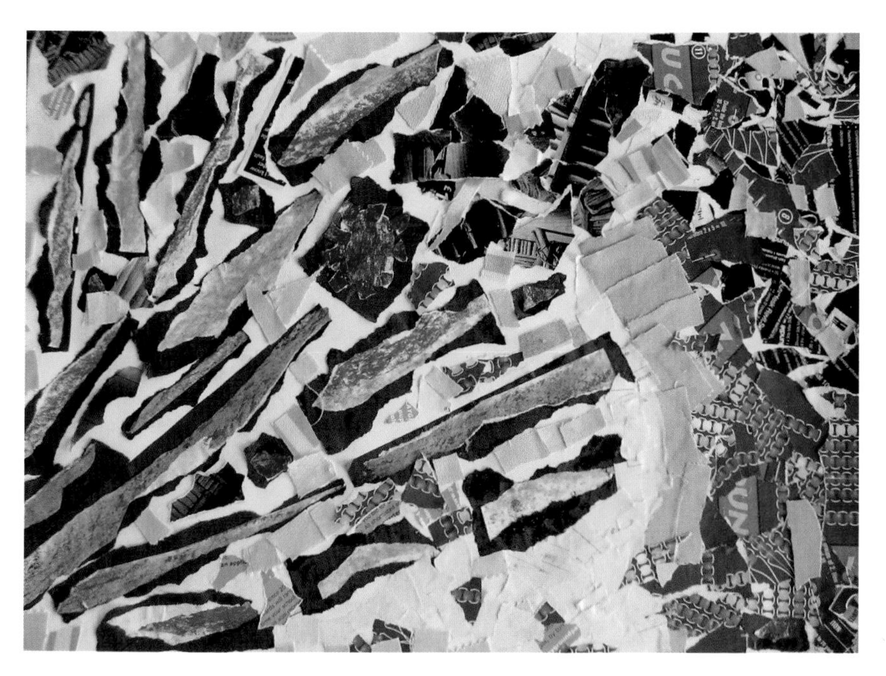

Lauren Crabb Age 9

Virus attack

Marvellously tight compact fireworks
zooming through cracks as they leak
whizzing and spinning round the sky
wild and free as they fly
scalding hot shapes and sizes
as lots more colours rise
all the colours scentless and extraordinary
swaying round wildly and merry
infected bubbles of scentless colour
all individual and not like each other
some so big they're almost like the mother
looks like rainbow sherbet nice and sweet
they're almost tempting to eat
marvellously bubbles just like they'll pop.

Jessica Millns Age 10

Max Allinson Age 11

The world beyond

It's like a jelly fish carrying a stone up to the surface,
it's like a snake swallowing a huge egg,
it's like an egg and a piece of ham on a plate,
it looks like a crab pinching a football,
it looks like a giant monster walking round the world,
it's like a toothless monster trying to crack an egg with his mouth,
it's like a bowling machine that's just brought back a bowling ball,
it's like a monster eating a giant pea but throwing bogies on the giant pea,
but no, it's just a cell eating an infected cell.

Joseph Rix Age 10

Virus vs. cells

I'm sick, there's nothing I can do but sleep.
Deep inside me a dark, evil virus is at work who is taking my cells captive
DC patrol cells spot the virus and tell king brain,
king brain sends in B reinforcement cells, who make antibodies,
the antibodies surround the virus and turn that space into a battlefield.
Ching, chang, chung,
the blades clung and king brain now sends in gobble cells
and tell disposal cells
the M cells gobble the virus up,
whilst the king cells dispose of the infected cells.
Who wins?
Me and my cells win!

Callum Cummings Age 9

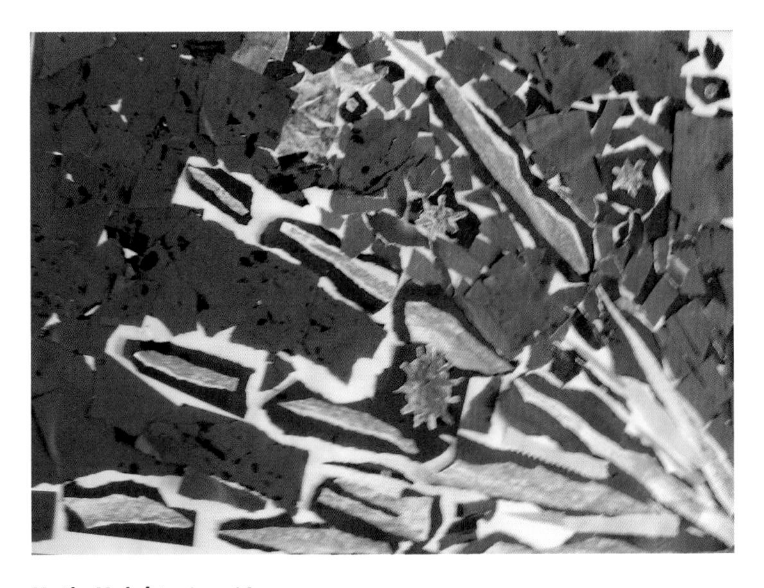

Katie Knights Age 10

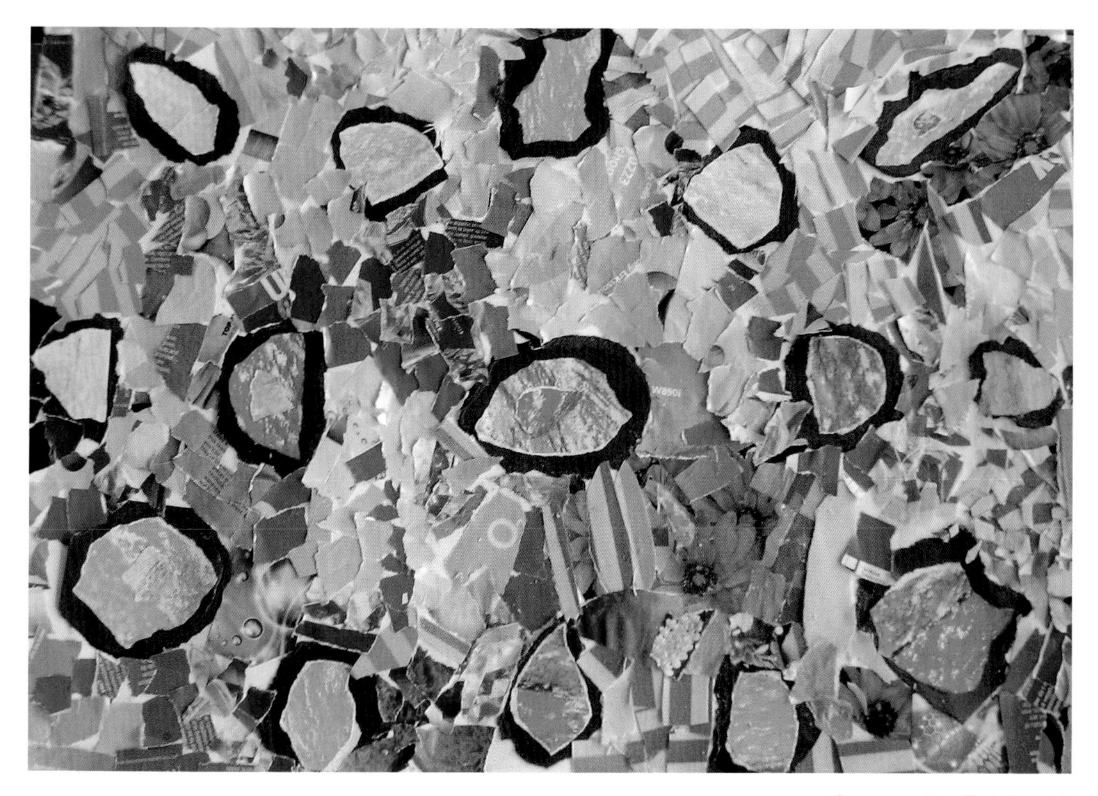

Shannon Parfitt Age 10

Planet dendrites

Viruses can make you very, very ill,
So go to the doctors and they'll give you a pill.
Pills are there to get rid of the pain,
then you'll never get a virus again.
But that's only a dream.

Some viruses are dull and some are grey,
and some are colourful; well that's what I'll say.
Some are big, some are small,
some are scary and some are nothing at all.

It's a tiny planet ever so small,
unlike for it to be rather tall,
little spots sparkling light
the background is as dead as night.

Chloe-Jane Davidson Age 10

Defends

Hell of black space touch the enamelled skin.
Space of island spread on the witch hat,
pushing the powerful bacteria to take the cell of forces.
Spots of yellow freedom on thy move to witchcraft.
Capture thy gloominess thou black mood.
Take the luminous feeling away.
Infected science rapid, of thy defence to shooting smoke.
Shaking movement take lightning sense.

Ruth Gayton Age 11

Jake Fitzsimmons Age 10

Interfaces

Gillian Rich
Institute of Food Research

The themes running through my work as a scientist relate to the physics, chemistry and biology of surfaces and interfaces. My biological research and teaching has mainly been on the biochemistry and physiology of membranes. When I joined the Institute of Food Research I became interested in human digestion and, in particular, how ingested fats and oils are broken down and absorbed into the body. A key stage in this process is the dispersal of the fat and oil into fine particles or droplets, aided by the presence of surface active agents. The resultant large oil/water interfacial area can be occupied by enzymes which break down the fats further into forms that can pass through the cells lining the intestine and thence into the blood. The expansion of air-water interfaces when you blow soap bubbles or make foams, is analogous to the expansion of oil-water interfaces when you make an emulsion. The stability of both depends on the presence of surface active agents, such as washing-up liquid, lipids and bile salts. These are what we used and had fun with on the SAW day.

Barford Primary School

Teacher **Nick King**
Age range of children **10–11**

Scientist **Gillian Rich**
Artist **Sarah Jarrett**
Writer **Martin Figura**

The children were very enthusiastic and did the experiments with some thought. They made pertinent observations on some things I thought they probably wouldn't notice. They used some of the equipment in a way I hadn't anticipated, which all added to their and my enjoyment!

Gillian Rich Scientist

For the children to have the chance to access the knowledge, inspiration and ideas of the three experts was terrific. They had a great day. The excitement of seeing the test tubes and equipment made them feel like they were 'in a real lab'. I will long remember their faces. The concept is superb. It works wonderfully and has informed my teaching during the last year.

Nick King Teacher

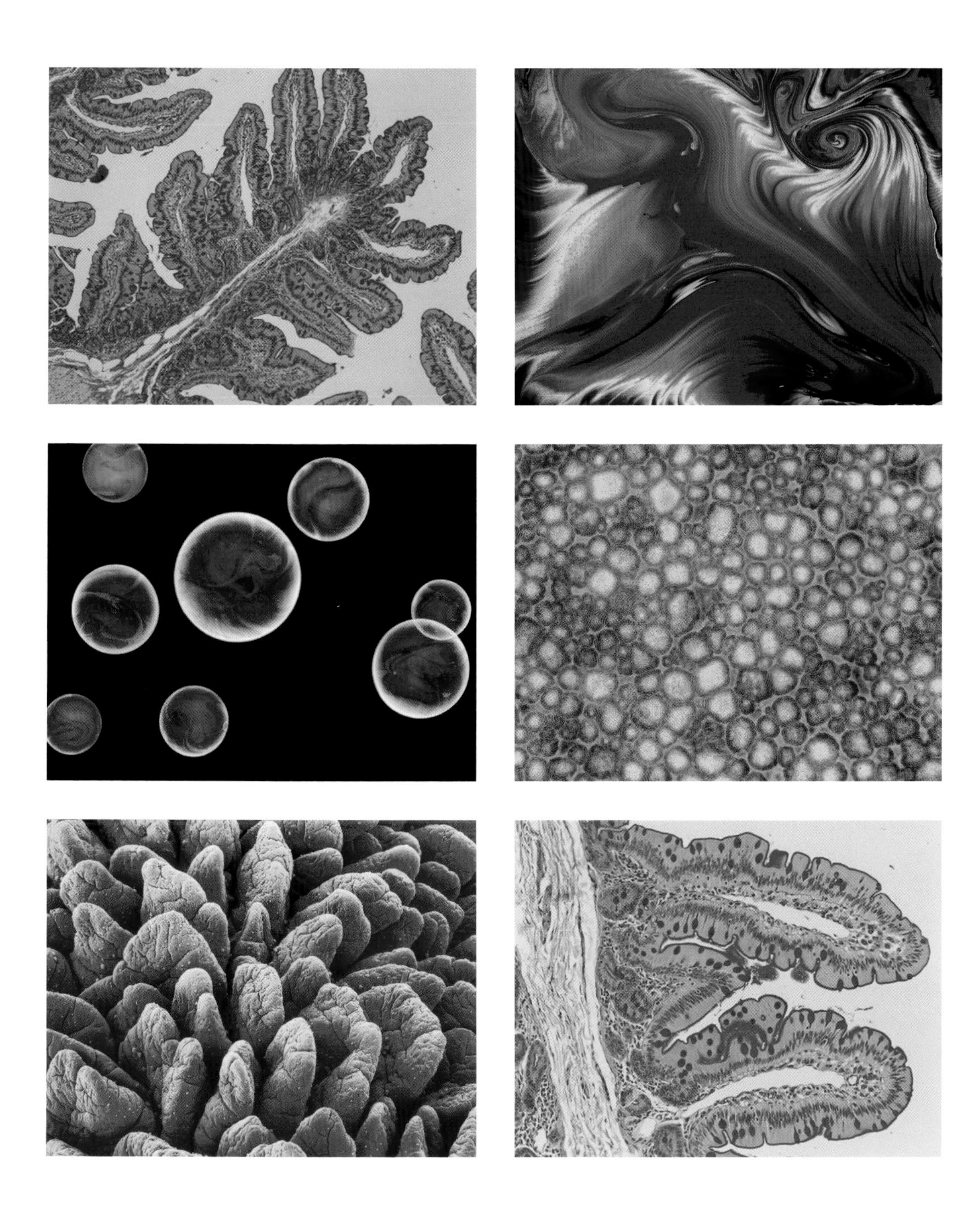

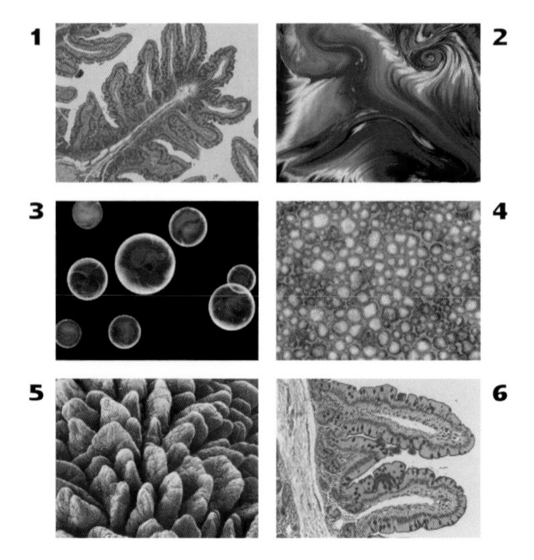

1 Light micrograph of villi on the lining of the jejunum, part of the small intestine. The lining has many folds, known as plicae circulares or Kerckring's valves, in this region. Both the plicae and villi serve to increase the surface area for the absorption of nutrients from the gut lumen. The folds are mainly composed of columnar epithelial cells (purple) interspersed with goblet cells (pink). The goblet cells secrete mucus, which lines the surface of the membrane.
Image: Innerspace Imaging/Science Photo Library.

2 Interference colours on illuminated soap film.
Image: Hermann Eisenbeiss/Science Photo Library.

3 Soap bubbles.
Image: Lawrence Lawry/Science Photo Library.

4 Coloured transmission electron micrograph (TEM) of liposome vesicles. These artificially constructed, spherical vesicles possess a selectively permeable wall that closely resembles the membrane of a living cell. They are used in biotechnology research to investigate the functioning of the cell membrane and, since they can be incorporated into living cells, are used to deliver drugs of high toxicity to specific cells in the body, such as cancer cells.
Image: David McCarthy/Science Photo Library.

5 Coloured scanning electron micrograph (SEM) of villi (folds) on the lining of the small intestine.
Image: Susumu Nishinaga/Science Photo Library.

6 Light micrograph of villi on the lining of the small intestine.
Image: Innerspace Imaging/Science Photo Library.

Amy Kirkham Age 9

Eden Mullane Age 11

My dinner

The sausage as smooth as a tongue,
the mashed potatoes as squishy as mud,
the sprouts as hard as a tyre,
the peas as small as a bud.

Anon Age 10/11

My dinner

It starts on the plate,
chips, peas and skate,
which I honestly hate,
into the mouth,
crunch crunch it goes,
down through the throat and the oesophagus,
into the stomach,
rumble, groan,
'This is great,' I say across the table,
'Don't speak with your mouth full'
replies my aunt Mabel.

Lauren Cooper Age 10

Olivia Dolman Age 10

Food molecules

Clare Mills
Institute of Food Research

Gerry Toole
Institute of Food Research

Louise Salt
Institute of Food Research

We are interested in understanding how molecules in food (proteins and carbohydrates, like starch and those found in plant cell walls) form different kinds of structures in the foods we eat. These structures affect the way food looks and its texture (crunchy, soft, smooth) and how it interacts with our bodies, affecting its nutritional quality. Cereal-based foods are important in this respect and we are especially interested in wheat and wheat-based foods like bread. For example, we have been studying how molecules and structures like starch granules affect the way bubbles form in bread. These bubbles are important in giving bread its light texture which consumers prefer. We have also been studying how different varieties of wheat and growing conditions affect the kinds of molecules found in grain cell walls. These are important because they make up the fraction we know as bran and fibre.

food molecules

Eaton Primary School

Teacher **Rosemary Mackie and Ros Earl**
Age range of children **8–9**

Scientists **Clare Mills, Gerry Toole and Louise Salt**
Artist **Chris Hann**
Writer **Tom Corbett**

Comments from children age 8–9:

The science experiments were fantastic.

We learned how to use a microscope and how to find the starch content of lots of food.

I liked wearing goggles and gloves. I felt like a real scientist.

What would have made the day better? Even more science!

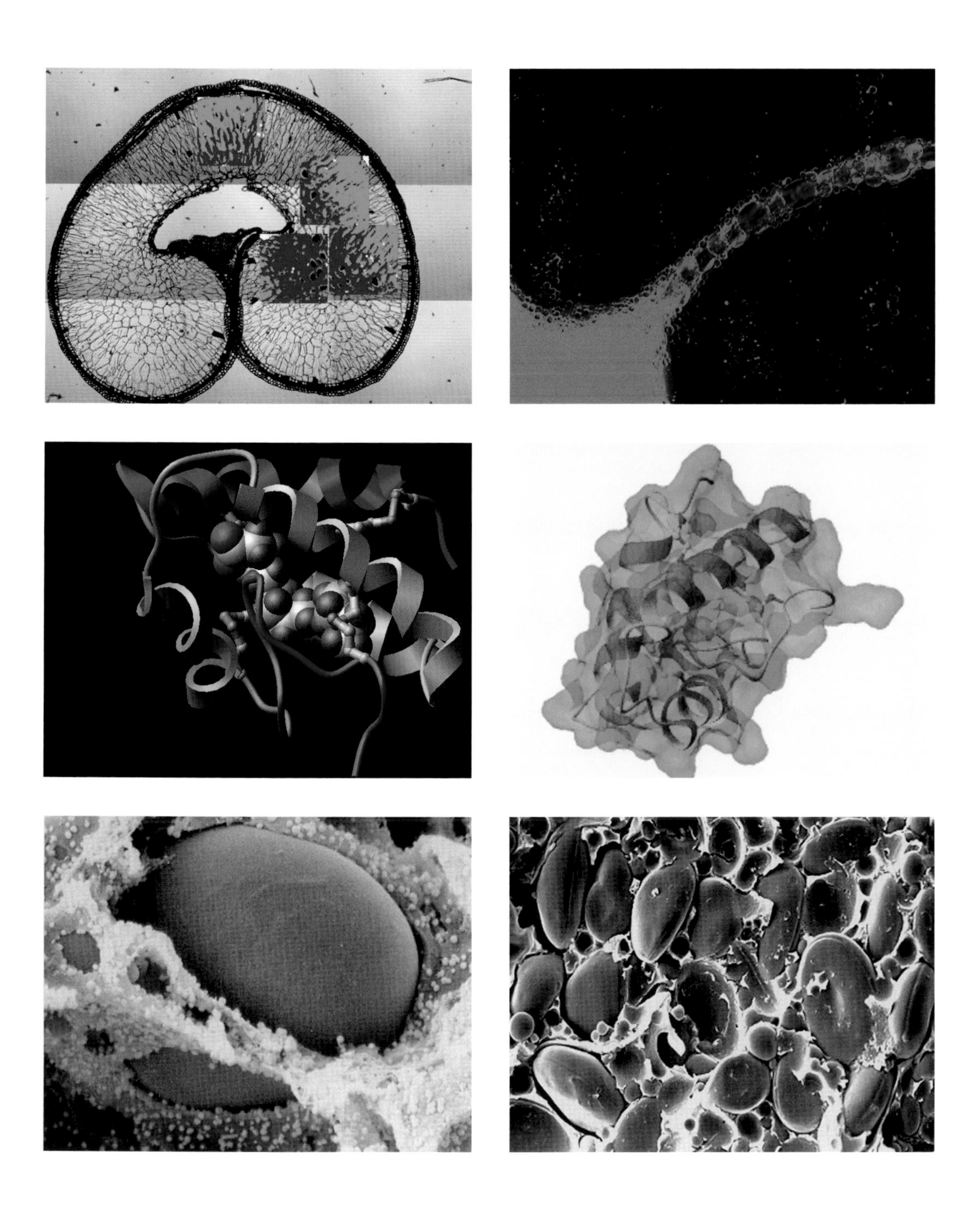

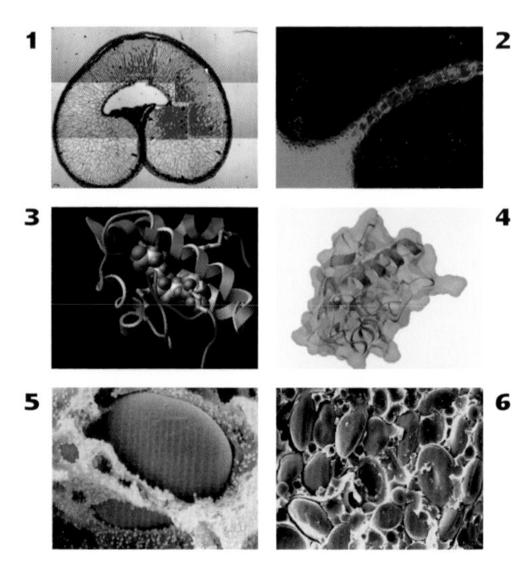

1 Section through a wheat grain from which all of the contents (starch, gluten, protein) have been removed to show the fine network of the cell walls. The superimposed coloured sections are derived from fourier transform infra-red (FT-IR) spectroscopic mapping of the cell's wall showing differences in the cell-wall polysaccharides across the endosperm.

Image: Geraldine Toole.

2 An epifluorescence micrograph of a bubble wall in bread dough. The section has been stained with Nile red, which fluoresces in the presence of lipid. The image shows how the starch granules in the dough align in the bubble wall, rather like stones in an arched bridge.

Image: Paul Gunning.

3 A model of a protein (non-specific lipid transfer protein) from barley shown as a ribbon. The molecule has a tunnel running through its centre in which lipid molecules sit. This structure has one-lipid molecules sitting in the tunnel – it's the part that looks like a caterpillar.

Image: John Jenkins.

4 Another model of a non-specific lipid transfer protein from barley, with the van der Waals forces shown as green shading around the molecule.

Image: John Jenkins.

5 Scanning electron micrograph (SEM) showing the freeze-fractured tissue from the central starchy endosperm of a wheat grain. The large round ball is an A-type starch granule, embedded in a protein matrix, which has been immunolabelled with silver-enhanced gold particles.

Image: Mary Parker. Reprinted from *Journal of Cereal Science* 41, E.N.C. Mills, M.L. Parker, N. Wellner, G. Toole, K. Feeney and P.R. Shewry. Chemical imaging: the distribution of ions and molecules in developing and mature wheat grain pp193–201 (2005), reproduced with permission from Elsevier.

6 Scanning electron micrograph (SEM) showing the freeze-fractured tissue from the central starchy endosperm of a wheat grain. The large oval-shaped particles are starch granules, the large ones being A-type and the smaller ones B-type granules. These are embedded in a background matrix of gluten protein.

Image: Mary Parker.

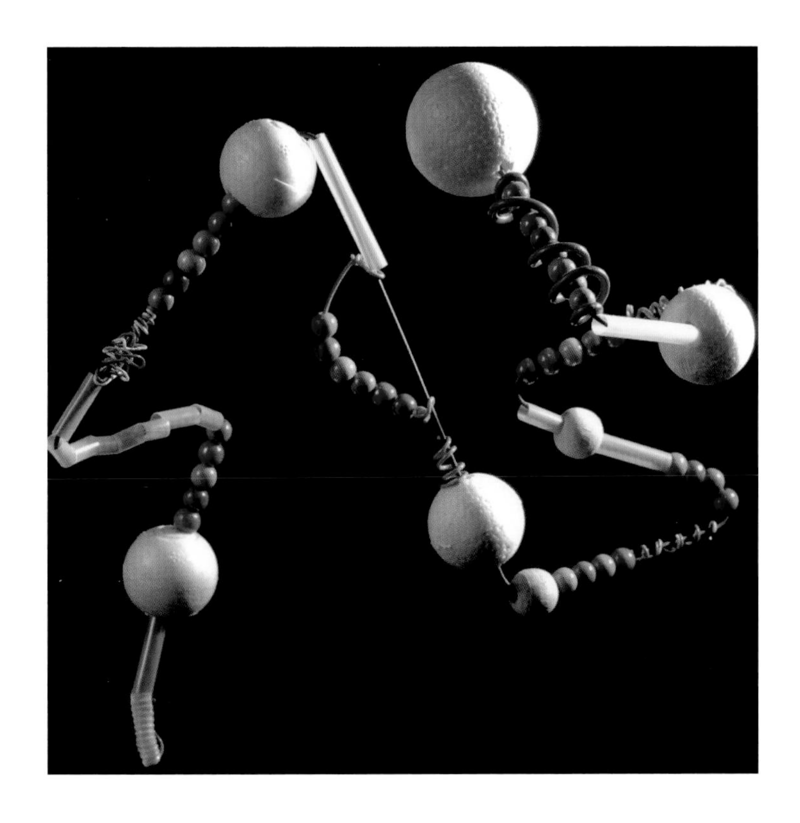

Heart

Heart with stones
you look so good
with those pebbles in you.

Niall Cole Age 8

The picture

Looks like the inside of
popcorn
or someone's
eyes or
an eyeball
or a
chocolate mini egg
or buttons on a shirt
or a pair of glasses
or a medal
or a head
or a
letter
or a
bubble
or an
ear
or a
ball
or the
glass of a microphone
or a
circle.

Callum Lake Age 8

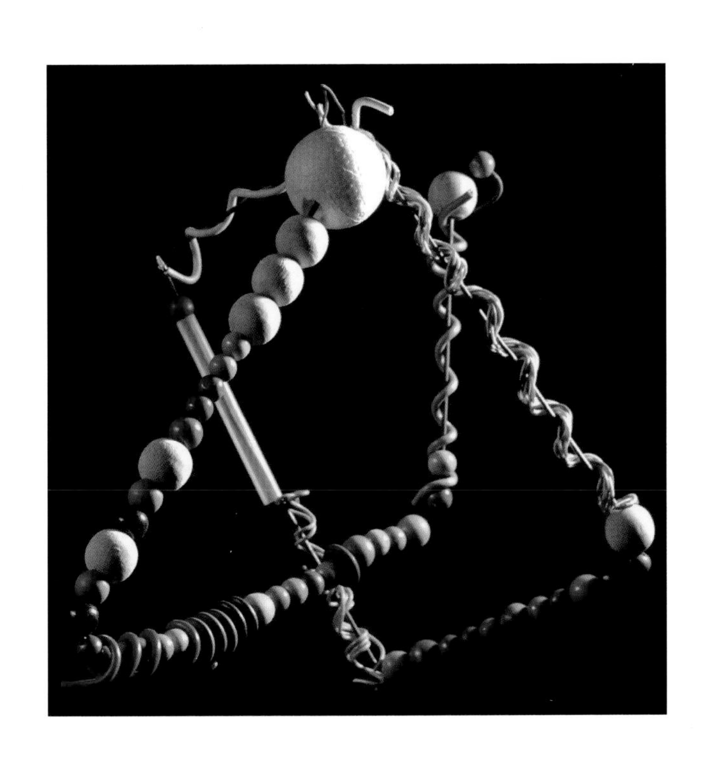

The thingy-mabob machine

I see balls.
I see pipes.
A machine of many colours.
A machine
making mysteries.
With springs,
pipes and joints,
It makes things
like bubbles,
like cloud and air,
like shine for the sun
dark for the night.
A thing no-one sees ...
Yet it's so bright
a name for this marvel,
a name for this thing ...
Hear it right now,
The Thingy-mabob Machine.

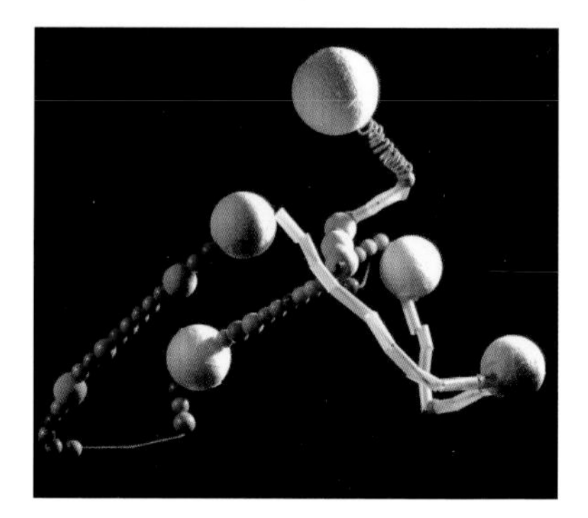

Emma Wilson Kemsley Age 9

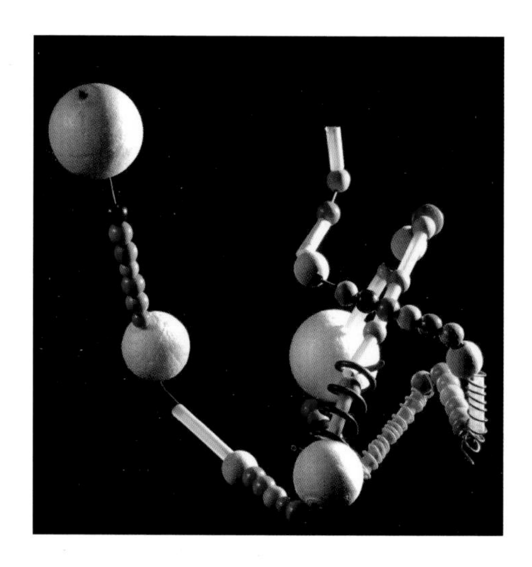

Plant development

Alexis Moschopoulos
John Innes Centre

Alexis is a PhD student studying leaf development. He is interested in how genes can act to determine organ shape. He is using a mutant approach to identify genes involved in leaf patterning. He's very interested in how some genes can affect leaf patterning, and how single changes in nucleic acids can have such dramatic effects on leaf shape.

Matilda is a third-year PhD student within a group working on the plant *Arabidopsis thaliana*. Her research focuses on understanding how the differences in starch granule morphology, size and number per chloroplast are determined.

Matilda Crumpton-Taylor
John Innes Centre

Halesworth Middle School

Teacher **Hetty van Wijk**
Age range of children **10–11**

Scientists **Alexis Moschopoulos and Matilda Crumpton-Taylor**
Artist **Sarah Jarrett**
Writer **Tom Corbett**

I learned that we are 2% banana.

Tom Allenby Age 11

I liked science best because we saw mutant plants.

Tom Allenby Age 11

I learned that you can make a poem from a little bit of DNA.

Ruby Brooks Age 10

I learned how to extract DNA from a banana.

Lewis Willard Age 11

It would have been good to have done the history of plants and where plants come from.

Elinor Pooley Age 11

What would have made the day better? If we got to eat the bananas.

Stephanie Gauthier Age 10

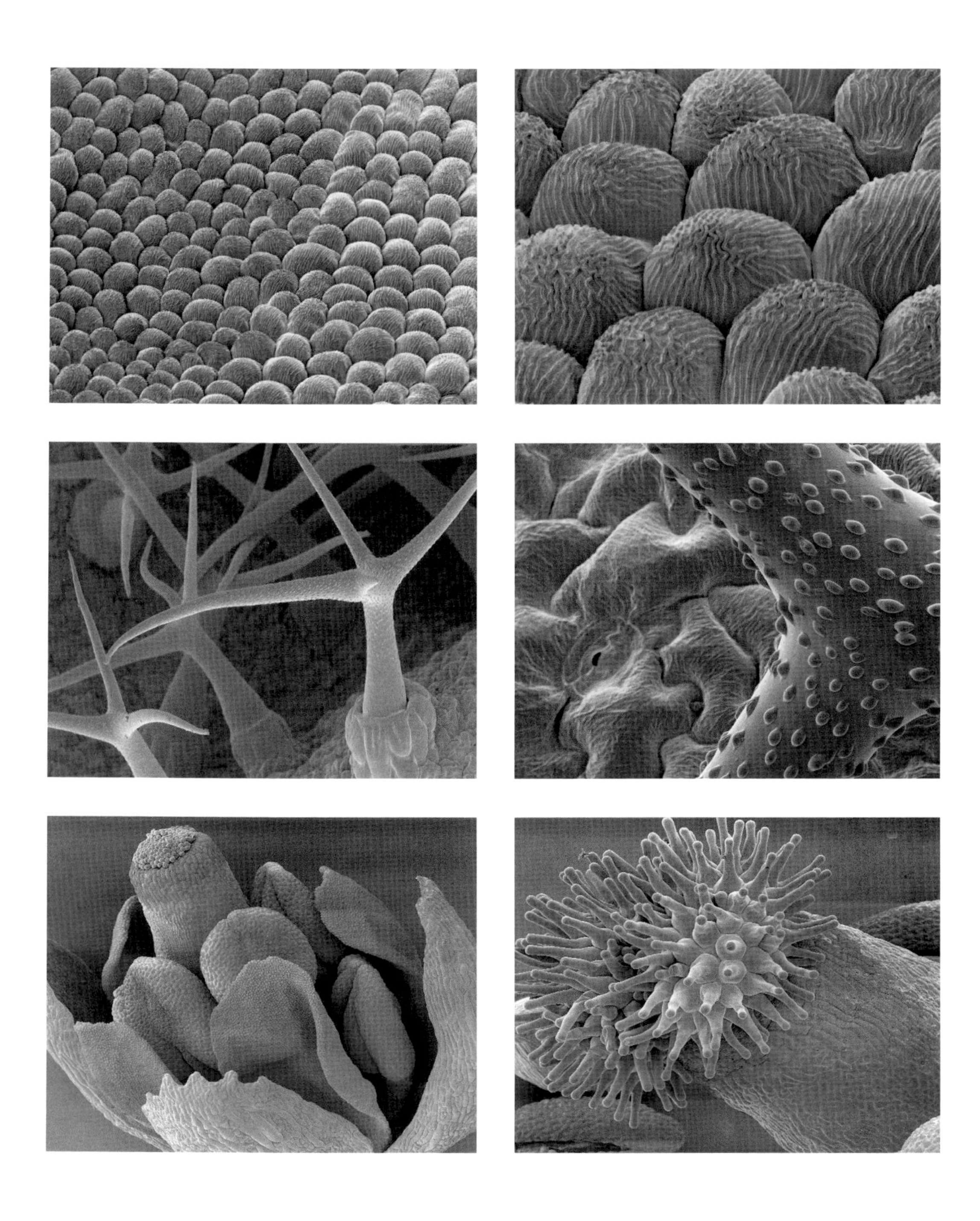

1 This is a scanning electron micrograph (SEM) of the inside surface of a petal from the flowering plant *Arabidopsis thaliana*. Each rounded unit is a cell, and inside each cell there is the DNA that instructs that cell how to act.
Image: Matilda Crumpton-Taylor.

2 This is a higher magnification of the same petal surface shown in image 1.
Image: Matilda Crumpton-Taylor.

3 These branched structures are called trichomes. They are single hair-like cells that are formed on the surface of leaves and have various functions including protecting plants from insects and from the sun's damaging rays.
Image: Alexis Moschopoulos

4 The trichome in the foreground is growing from the cell surface in the background, on an *Arabidopsis* leaf. The cells at the leaf surface have a jigsaw-puzzle piece shape, and you can see the opening of a stomata at the left. The leaf cells have collapsed due to processing prior to imaging with a scanning electron microscope (SEM).
Image: Alexis Moschopoulos.

5 This SEM shows the organs of an *Arabidopsis* flower: sepals, petals, stamens and the carpel. The pollen is produced on the stamen heads, which is placed onto the carpel to produce seeds. You can see the variation of cell shape and size as well as the differences in organ size and shape.
Image: Matilda Crumpton-Taylor.

6 A close-up of the stigma at the tip of a carpel of an *Arabidopsis* flower shows the alien, bushy shape the stigma forms when it is ready to be fertilized by the pollen from the nearby stamen.
Image: Matilda Crumpton-Taylor.

W

O

R

M

infested chocolate bonbons

Flavoured bonbons

Chocolate

Cells

Barnacle shells

Barnacles

Sea sized barnacle

Small sized barnacles

Large sized barnacles

Old and wise barnacles

Stones

Old stones

Large stones

Small stones

Michiel Derks Age 11

Cells

The
cell of
a white flower
like the hard scales of a dragon,
white, milk, and dark chocolate truffles in a
chocolate factory, the tops of evergreens of a forest
from a birds eye view all compact, lots of honey fungi
on a undisturbed forest floor in Canada, water snails multiplying
like bacteria, a huge mountain range in Nepal or Italy.

Tim Lawrence Age 11

Bethany Clouting Age 10

My pig

The image in my eyes
is a pig's face,
with eyes,
nose and hair
a rocket
shooting into the air.

A plant
being explored by tiny people
a man
an ugly man
a wrinkly man.

An old man
a funny man
with a big nose
sticking out,
a manta ray
swimming in the sea.

A mouth eating a plant
a flower opening up
a face always staring

Pig.

Izaak Loader Age 10

My wrinkly flower

Someone's leather jacket,
crinkly and scaly.

Sand, when it's had water over it,
and has suddenly dried up,
leaving it in an odd pattern.

Like pencil sharpenings,
that have been scattered across the table.

It looks like a cape,
protecting you.

Iona Champain Age 11

Stigma

Pickled gherkin
with acorn parasite.
Punk with an afro.
Horror movie slug.
Weird alien.

Thousands of eyes
stretching on long stalks
to the stars
crawling like a snail.

Jake Savage Age11

Arron Sayer Age 11

Ben Armour-Chelu Age 11

What is it?

Tennis balls put in a pile.
People's heads in a big crowd.
Coral at the bottom of the sea
and the nicest chocolate in a box for me.

It really is a close-up of flower cells!

I thought it was...
tennis balls
in a pile
people's heads
in a big crowd
coral at the bottom of the sea
and the nicest chocolates in a box for me.
But I was wrong and I guess that is just silly me!!!

It really is a close-up of flower cells!

Stephanie Gauthier Age 11

Trichomes

Chickens legs
spider web
tentacles
three-fingered hand
spiky stuff
waving in the dark sea
stringy cheese
plant roots in disguise
DNA, DNA
that's the way
Oooooooooooooooooooo.

Ben Armour-Chelu and
Bram Chilton Smiley Age 11

Bumps
lumps
chocolate chunks
planet stumps
jigsaw shapes
seascapes
blobs
splashes, crashes,
smashes
tumbles
rumbles
little image

stomata, trichome,
big pointy cell in a leaf.

DNA.

Zoe Stannard Age 11

Hannah Leech Age 11

Weird balls

Chocolate balls
meat balls (round and lumpy)
exercise balls (squidgy)
plant buds (pointed a bit at the top)
hills (tall and round)
bonbons
cells
profiteroles
truffles
eggs (oval)
cupcakes
stones
sea shells
sheep (fluffy)
heads.

Callum Anthony and Owen Davies Age 11